Personal Tax

(Finance Act 2019)

Workbook

for assessments from January 2020

Aubrey Penning
Bob Thomas

Published by Osborne Books Limited
Tel 01905 748071
Email books@osbornebooks.co.uk
Website www.osbornebooks.co.uk

Design by Laura Ingham

Printed by CPI Group (UK) Limited, Croydon, CR0 4YY, on environmentally friendly, acid-free paper from managed forests.

British Library Cataloguing in Publication Data
A catalogue record for this book is available from the British Library

ISBN 978-1-911198-39-0

Contents

Also available from Osborne Books...

Tutorials

Clear, explanatory books written
precisely to the specifications

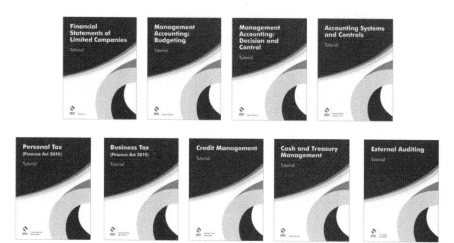

Student Zone

Login to access your free ebooks and
interactive revision crosswords

Introduction

Qualifications covered

This book has been written specifically to cover the Unit 'Personal Tax' which is an optional Unit for the following qualifications:

AAT Professional Diploma in Accounting – Level 4

AAT Professional Diploma in Accounting at SCQF – Level 8

This book contains Chapter Activities which provide extra practice material in addition to the activities included in the Osborne Books Tutorial text, and Practice Assessments to prepare the student for the computer based assessments. The latter are based directly on the structure, style and content of the sample assessment material provided by the AAT at www.aat.org.uk.

Suggested answers to the Chapter Activities and Practice Assessments are set out in this book.

Osborne Study and Revision Materials

The materials featured on the previous page are tailored to the needs of students studying this Unit and revising for the assessment. They include:

- **Tutorials:** paperback books with practice activities
- **Student Zone:** access to Osborne Books online resources
- **Osborne Books App:** Osborne Books ebooks for mobiles and tablets

Visit www.osbornebooks.co.uk for details of study and revision resources and access to online material.

Exams, Finance Acts and tax years

This book has been designed to include guidance and exercises based on Tax Year 2019/20 (Finance Act 2019). We understand that the AAT plan to assess this legislation from 1 January 2020 to 31 December 2020. Tutors and students are advised to check this with the AAT and ensure that they sit the correct computer based assessment.

Chapter
activities

1 Introduction to income tax

1.1 State whether each of the following statements is true or false.

		True	False
(a)	Different tax systems are based on different views of which are the most important tax principles and how they should be applied		
(b)	The principle of equity means that every taxpayer should pay the same amount of tax, regardless of their circumstances		
(c)	Vertical equity means that taxation is fair at different levels in society		
(d)	Although tax is often used in an attempt to change behaviour, this conflicts with the principle of neutrality		
(e)	A progressive tax system is one in which the same proportion of income is paid in tax for all income levels		
(f)	A tax system that charges every taxpayer the same percentage of their income in tax is a proportional system		

1.2 State whether each of the following statements is true or false.

		True	False
(a)	It is not the taxpayer's responsibility to inform HMRC of any untaxed taxable income, unless they have been asked to complete a tax return		
(b)	Accountants must normally follow the rules of confidentiality, but there are exceptions		
(c)	Where a practitioner has knowledge or suspicion that his client is money laundering, then he has a duty to inform the relevant person or authority		
(d)	Accountants should warn clients if they suspect money laundering to give the client a chance to cease the activity		
(e)	When an accountant is advising a client the greatest duty of care is to the client		

1.3 State which of the following can provide sources of information about tax law and its interpretation.

	Yes	No
(a) HMRC extra-statutory concessions		
(b) Statute law		
(c) HMRC statements of practice		
(d) Case law		
(e) Website www.gov.uk		
(f) HMRC guides and help sheets		

1.4 Match the following examples of income with the correct income category.

Sample Income	Income Category
UK dividends	Property Income
Partnership profits	Savings and Investment Income
Rents from land	Trading Income
Earnings from a job	Employment, Pension and Social Security Income

1.5 Tick the columns to show which of the following categories of income is taxed on an accruals basis, and which is normally on a receipts basis (ie based on when received).

Income Category	Accruals basis	Receipts basis
(a) Property Income		
(b) Savings and Investment Income		
(c) Trading Income		
(d) Employment, Pension and Social Security Income		

1.6 State which of the following types of income are exempt from income tax.

Income Category	Exempt	Not exempt
(a) Employment income		
(b) Income from an ISA		
(c) Premium bond prizes		
(d) Rent received from a buy-to-let property		
(e) Betting winnings (unless a professional gambler)		
(f) Lottery prizes		

1.7 Analyse the following list of statements by ticking the appropriate column.

Statement	True	False
(a) UK residence is determined by some specific tests that are applied to the individual for each tax year		
(b) An individual who lives permanently in the UK can choose the domicile of any country in the world, simply by completing the relevant form		
(c) An individual who is resident and domiciled in the UK will pay UK tax on their worldwide income and gains		
(d) An individual who is resident in the UK, but not UK domiciled or 'deemed domiciled' will pay UK tax on income and gains arising in the UK		
(e) An individual who is resident in the UK, but not UK domiciled or 'deemed domiciled' will never pay UK tax on income and gains arising in the rest of the world		
(f) An individual who is resident in the UK, but not UK domiciled or 'deemed domiciled' can elect to pay UK tax on their overseas income on a remittance basis, but there is normally a substantial charge for this basis to apply		

2   Income from property

2.1   Chester has two properties in addition to his home, details of which are as follows:

Two bedroom house:

(1)   This unfurnished house is rented out for £850 per month payable on 6th of each month. The property was occupied this tax year until 1 February when the tenants suddenly moved out, owing the rent for January. Chester knows that he will not recover this rent. The property was let again from 1 May to another family.

(2)   Chester had to pay £530 for redecoration in March following the poor condition of the property at that time.

(3)   The only other expense paid by Chester on the house was 10% management charge to the agent on rent received.

One bedroom flat:

(1)   This furnished flat is rented out for £550 per month. The property was rented all tax year.

(2)   Chester paid council tax and water rates on the flat, totalling £1,100 for the period that the flat was occupied. He also paid buildings and contents insurance of £340 for the year.

Calculate the profit or loss made on each property, using the following table.

	Two bedroom house £	One bedroom flat £
Income		
Expenses:		

2.2 Stephan rents out one furnished property. The following is a statement compiled from his accounting records relating to the tax year.

	£	£
Rental Income Received		12,000
less expenditure:		
Council Tax	700	
Water Rates	300	
Insurance	380	
Cost of replacement furniture	2,100	
Depreciation of furniture	800	
Managing Agent's Charges	1,200	
		5,480
Profit		6,520

Required:

Calculate the assessable property income for Stephan, using the following table.

	£	£
Income		
Expenditure:		
Assessable Income		

2.3 The following list of expenditure relates to a rental property.

Analyse the expenditure according to its tax treatment.

Expenditure	Allowable	Not allowable
(a) Replacement of washing machine		
(b) Legal fees relating to purchase of property		
(c) Cleaning property between tenancies		
(d) Legal fees relating to tenancy agreement		
(e) Renovation of property between purchase and first tenancy		
(f) Insurance against non-recoverable rent		

2.4 The following expenditure was incurred during a void period between tenancies.

Analyse the expenditure according to its tax treatment.

Expenditure	Allowable	Not allowable
(a) Internal redecoration		
(b) Replacement of carpets		
(c) Mortgage interest (adjusted proportion)		
(d) Property insurance		
(e) Mortgage repayments of capital		
(f) Advertising for tenants		

3 Income from savings and investments

3.1 Analyse the following statements into those that are true and those that are false.

	True	False
(a) There is no dividend allowance available for additional rate taxpayers		
(b) Income that falls within the personal savings allowance will still be treated as using up the tax bands and can result in savings or dividend income being pushed into a higher tax band		
(c) There is no personal savings allowance available for additional rate taxpayers		
(d) The personal savings allowance can be used to save tax on savings income or dividend income		

General real up

3.2 An individual has the following income before deduction of the personal allowance:

General Income   £20,000

Savings Income   £1,500

Dividend Income   £2,000

Calculate the amount of income tax payable on each of these categories of income, and in total.

S+D

3.3 An individual has the following income before deduction of the personal allowance:

General Income   £25,000

Savings Income   £3,500   *S+D*

Dividend Income   £6,000

Calculate the amount of income tax payable on each of these categories of income, and in total.

3.4 An individual has the following income before deduction of the personal allowance:

General Income   £60,000

Savings Income   £7,500

Dividend Income   £5,000

S+D

Calculate the amount of income tax payable on each of these categories of income, and in total.

3.5 The following statements relate to Individual Savings Accounts (ISAs). Identify which statements are true and which are false.

	True	False
(a) Cash ISAs can only be opened by individuals aged 18 or over who are UK resident		
(b) Stocks and shares ISAs can be used for shares in listed companies and government securities (gilts)		
(c) The interest and / or dividends received from investment in ISAs are tax free and do not utilise the personal savings allowance or dividend allowance		
(d) Each individual can only invest in one cash ISA, one stocks and shares ISA and one innovative finance ISA in a tax year		
(e) Cash ISAs can only be transferred to another provider at the end of a tax year		
(f) ISAs cannot be held in joint names, and individual investors must be UK resident		

ISA)

4 Income from employment

4.1 Complete the following table by correctly matching the indicators as relating to employment or self employment.

Indicators of Employment	Indicators of Self Employment

Indicators

- Choose work hours and invoice for work done
- Need to do the work yourself
- Told how, where and when to do work
- No risk of capital or losses
- Work for several people or organisations
- Decide yourself how, when and where to do work
- Can employ helper or substitute
- Employer provides equipment
- Risk own capital and bear losses from work that is not to standard
- Work set hours and paid regular wage with sick pay and holidays
- Usually work for one employer
- Provide own equipment

4.2 **(a)** What scale charge percentage would be applied for petrol cars with the following CO_2 emissions?

    (1)   44 g/km

    (2)   134 g/km

    (3)   151 g/km

    (4)   249 g/km

(b) Silvia was provided with a secondhand car on 6 October 2019. It cost the company £8,000, but the list price of this car when bought new was £17,000. The car has a CO_2 emission of 168 g/km, and has a diesel engine. The company pays for all running costs, except private fuel.

    (1) The cost of the car used in the benefit in kind computation is

        £ [   ]

    (2) The percentage used in the benefit in kind computation is

        [   ] %

    (3) The assessable benefit for Silvia relating to the car for 2019/20 is

        £ [   ]

4.3 **(a)** When accommodation is purchased by an employer, what is the value of the property above which an additional benefit is applied?

(a)	£60,000	
(b)	£70,000	
(c)	£75,000	
(d)	£80,000	
(e)	£100,000	
(f)	£125,000	

(b) Would the following situations be treated as being job-related where no accommodation benefit arises?

		Yes	No
(a)	House provided for a vicar		
(b)	House provided by employer for accountant working for a housing association		
(c)	Flat in sheltered accommodation provided for an on-site care manager		

(c) Summer was provided with accommodation in the form of a flat that the employer purchased recently for £165,000. It is not job related. The flat has an annual value of £9,300. Summer pays £200 per month towards the private use of the flat. Assume that the HMRC official interest rate is 2.5%. Her taxable benefit is:

(a)	£6,900	
(b)	£9,300	
(c)	£9,150	
(d)	£11,550	

4.4 On 6 December 2019, Kevin was provided with a company loan of £16,000 on which he pays interest at 1.0% per annum. On 6 February 2020 Kevin repaid £2,000. The official rate of interest is 2.5%.

What is the benefit in kind for 2019/20 to the nearest £?

4.5 **(a)** Dee uses her own car for business travelling. During the tax year she travelled 11,500 business miles for which she was paid 50p per mile by her employer. The impact of this is:

(a)	She will have a taxable amount of £575	
(b)	She will have a taxable amount of £875	
(c)	She will claim an allowable expense of £875	
(d)	She will claim an allowable expense of £575	

(b) Eddie has an occupational pension scheme to which he contributes 5% of his salary. His employer contributes 6% of his salary. His salary was £28,400. The impact of this is:

(a)	His taxable salary will be increased by £1,704	
(b)	His taxable salary will be reduced by £1,420	
(c)	His taxable salary will be increased by £284	
(d)	His basic rate band will be extended by £1,775	

(c) Steve pays £300 per year in subscriptions to professional bodies. His employer reimburses him £180. The overall impact of this is:

(a)	No impact on tax	
(b)	An allowable deduction of £120	
(c)	A benefit of £180	
(d)	An allowable deduction of £300	

(d) Genna has a non-contributory occupational pension scheme. This means:

(a)	The employer pays a percentage of her salary into the scheme, but Genna does not	
(b)	Genna pays a percentage of her salary into the scheme, but the employer does not	
(c)	Only the Government pays a percentage of her salary into the scheme	
(d)	Genna and the Government both pay a percentage of her salary into the scheme	

5 Preparing income tax computations

5.1 John has the following income for the tax year:

Employment income	£57,500
Rental income	£10,350
Bank account interest	£700
Dividends	£6,500

John paid £3,200 (net) into a private pension scheme, and made gift aid payments totalling £1,600 (net).

Using the following table, calculate the total Income Tax liability for John.

	£
Employment income	
Rental income	
Savings income	
Dividend income	
Less Personal Allowance	
Taxable income	
Tax Calculation:	

5.2 Dave and Sue are a married couple with a joint savings account that produces annual savings income of £4,000. They have no other savings income.

Dave has general income of £20,000, and Sue has general income of £55,000.

Complete the following table to show for each person, the annual Income Tax on the savings income only based on three alternative situations:

- The current situation

- If all the savings were held in Dave's name

- If all the savings were held in Sue's name

Tax savg

Situation	Dave's tax on savings income £	Sue's tax on savings income £
Current position		
All savings in Dave's name		
All savings in Sue's name		

5.3 Karen has employment income of £50,000, plus normal profits from a rental property of £8,000 per year. She is considering whether to spend an additional £6,000 on replacement carpets and curtains for the rental property.

Tax Deductl Complete the following table.

	Normal situation £	Replacing carpet and curtains £
Taxable Income		
Tax at 20%		
Tax at 40%		
Total Income Tax		
Net Cost of Replacements		

Adjust Sal

5.4 Wayne earns £45,000 per year from his job as a Sales Manager, and is entitled to a diesel company car and all fuel (business and private). The car has a list price of £22,000, but was purchased at a discount for £19,500. It has emissions of 144 g/km.

Wayne makes cash contributions of £1,600 per year into a personal pension scheme.

Calculate Wayne's tax liability (to the nearest £), using the following table.

Workings:		£
Salary		
Car benefit		
Fuel benefit		
Personal allowance		
Taxable income		
Tax at 20%:		
Tax at 40%:		
Total tax liability		

5.5 Rachel had employment income of £91,500 and received dividends of £17,500. She paid £1,200 (net) into a personal pension scheme.

Calculate her total income tax liability (ie before deduction of tax paid) for the tax year, using the table given below. Show tax to nearest £.

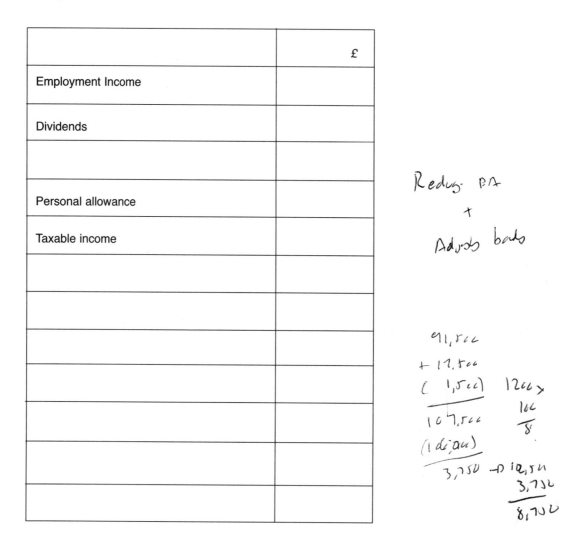

	£
Employment Income	
Dividends	
Personal allowance	
Taxable income	

Reduce PA
+
Adjusts bands

91,500
+ 17,500
(1,500)   1200 x
──────   100
107,500   8
(1 djau)
          3,750 → 12,5u
                3,750
              ─────
                8,700

↑ BR band by 100/80 £ PPIG. ft ad)
↓ PA by 50% (excess ann 100,000) → i.e £c al 420,000
↑ incn iaddo oth debs grad up pp lun ad o pu

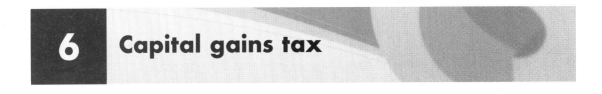

6 Capital gains tax

6.1 For each statement, tick the appropriate box.   BASIS

	Actual proceeds used	Deemed proceeds used	No gain or loss basis
(a) Father gives an asset to his son			
(b) Wife sells an asset to her husband			
(c) Simon gives an asset to his friend			
(d) Margaret sells an asset to her cousin for £15,000 when the market value is £40,000			
(e) Brian gives an asset to his civil partner, Dave			

6.2 Alex bought an asset in January 2008 for £36,000, selling it in the tax year for £35,000. He paid auctioneer's commission of 4% when he bought the asset and 5% when he sold the asset.

The loss on this asset is:

C+h cr Jde

(a)	£nil	
(b)	£1,000	
(c)	£4,190	
(d)	£2,440	

Legal fees are an allowable deduction where they relate to the purchase or sale of an asset.

TRUE / FALSE

6.3 State whether each of the following statements is true or false:

		True	False
(a)	The annual exemption is applied after capital losses are deducted		
(b)	Capital losses from the same year cannot safeguard the annual exemption		
(c)	Capital losses can be set against gains of the previous tax year		
(d)	Capital losses brought forward can safeguard the annual exemption when offset against current year gains		

6.4 Josie has a capital loss brought forward of £4,000. She is a higher rate income tax payer.

She sold an asset during the tax year for £19,000. She had been given the asset by her husband when it was worth £8,000. Her husband originally paid £6,500 for the asset.

Complete the following sentences:

(a) The gain on the asset is £

(b) The amount of loss that will be relieved is £

(c) The capital gains tax payable is £

(d) The loss to be carried forward to the next tax year is £

6.5 Complete the following table to show which assets are exempt from capital gains tax and which are chargeable.

Asset	Exempt	Chargeable
Antique furniture valued at £30,000		
Principal private residence		
Clock		
Shares		
Holiday home		
Government securities		
Vintage car		
Land		

6.6   Richard bought a house on 1 January 2002 for £125,000. He lived in the house until 31 December 2004 when he moved abroad for one year to work. He returned from abroad on 31 December 2005, and then immediately moved into his elderly father's house until 30 June 2007, leaving his own home empty. He then moved back into his own house until 31 December 2014, when he moved to a new home and put the house on the market. The house was eventually sold on 1 January 2020 for £205,000.

(a)   Which periods are treated as occupied and which are not?

Occupation / Deemed Occupation	Non-occupation

(b)   What is the chargeable gain on the property?

£ [ ]

6.7 The following table relates to sales of chattels.

Match the statements shown below to the correct asset details.

Asset	Sale proceeds	Cost	Statement
1	£4,000	£7,000	
2	£14,000	£8,000	
3	£8,000	£3,000	
4	£3,000	£5,000	
5	£15,000	£21,000	

Chattels (handwritten)

Statements:
- Exempt asset
- Calculate gain as normal
- Calculate loss as normal
- Sale proceeds to be £6,000
- Chattel marginal relief applies

6.8 Paul bought 20,000 shares in Lincoln Ltd for £5 per share in October 2000. He received a bonus issue of 1 for 25 shares in March 2003. In January 2020, Paul sold 8,000 shares for £9 per share.

Clearly showing the balance of shares, and their value, to carry forward, calculate the gain made on these shares. All workings must be shown in your calculations.

shares (handwritten)

7 Inheritance tax

7.1 Elizabeth died, leaving an estate of £800,000. She had not made any lifetime transfers. In her will she left the following:

- £250,000 to her husband, Phil

- £5,000 to charity

The balance of her estate to her son, Robert, including a home worth £300,000.

Calculate the Inheritance Tax due on the estate, and how much Robert will receive.

To D
Residue

7.2 Paul and Mary had been married for several years, when Mary died. Mary had not made any lifetime transfers. Mary left £40,000 to each of their two sons and the balance to Paul, including a home. Mary's estate was valued at £350,000.

Three years after Mary's death, Paul died. He had not made any lifetime transfers. His estate was worth £950,000 including a home worth £350,000, to be divided equally between his two sons.

Calculate the Inheritance Tax due on:

- Mary's estate

- Paul's estate

Spus To D
residual

7.3 Christine did not make any lifetime transfers in the previous tax year. During the current tax year she made the following gifts (shown in chronological order):

- £10,000 to her daughter, Rosy, when she got married

- £5,000 to her son, Robert, when he got divorced

- £1,000 to charity

- £500 to the Labour Party

- £2,500 to her parents to pay for them to go on holiday

- £15,000 to her husband, Roger, to buy a new car

Calculate the amount of each potentially exempt transfer made in the current tax year. Show clearly the use of each annual exemption where applicable.

7.4 Jonathan (who had not made any other transfers in recent tax years) made the following lifetime transfers:

31 December 2017 £170,000 payment into a trust (a chargeable transfer)

30 April 2018   £20,000 to his son, David

31 May 2018   £30,000 to his daughter, Masie on her birthday

On 30 September 2019, Jonathan died and left an estate valued at £630,000. It did not include a home. Jonathan's will listed the following beneficiaries:

- £250,000 to be paid to his wife, Julie

- £5,000 to be given to charity

- The balance to be shared equally between David and Masie

Required:

Calculate:

- The inheritance Tax payable during Jonathan's lifetime

- The inheritance Tax payable on Jonathan's death

Lifetime Trusts

7.5 Jim had made no lifetime transfers. When he died he left an estate valued at £800,000 and the following bequests:

- £200,000 to his wife

- £100,000 to charity

- The balance to his daughter, including a home valued at £300,000

Tap

Calculate:

- The Inheritance Tax payable

- The amount that his daughter will receive

Answers to chapter activities

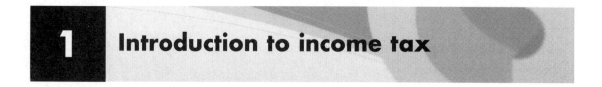

1 Introduction to income tax

1.1 (b) and (e) False; the remaining statements True

1.2 (a) and (d) False; (b), (c) and (e) True

1.3 All the options can provide sources of information about tax law and its interpretation.

1.4

Sample Income		Income Category
UK dividends	→	Savings and Investment Income
Partnership profits	→	Trading Income
Rents from land	→	Property Income
Earnings from a job	→	Employment, Pension and Social Security Income

1.5 (c) Accruals basis; (a), (b) and (d) Receipts basis

1.6 (b), (c), (e) and (f) Exempt; (a) and (d) Not exempt

1.7 (a), (c), (d) and (f) True; (b) and (e) False

2 Income from property

2.1

	Two bedroom house	One bedroom flat
	£	£
Income	7,650	6,600
Expenses:		
Management fees	765	
Redecoration	530	
Council Tax & Water		1,100
Insurance		340
Profit	6,355	5,160

2.2

	£	£
Income		12,000
Expenditure:		
Council tax	700	
Water rates	300	
Insurance	380	
Managing agent's charges	1,200	
Replacement furniture	2,100	
		4,680
Assessable Income		7,320

2.3   (a), (c), (d) and (f) Allowable; (b) and (e) Not allowable

2.4   (a), (b), (c), (d) and (f) Allowable; (e) Not allowable

3 Income from savings and investments

3.1 (b) and (c) True; (a) and (d) False

3.2

General Income	£20,000.00	
Less personal allowance	£12,500.00	
Taxable	£7,500.00	
Income tax £7,500.00 x 20%		£1,500.00
Savings Income	£1,500.00	
Income tax £1,000 x 0%		£0.00
£500 x 20%		£100.00
Dividend Income	£2,000.00	
Covered by dividend allowance		
Income tax £2,000.00 x 0%		£0.00
Total Income Tax		£1,600.00

3.3

General Income	£25,000.00		
Less personal allowance	£12,500.00		
Taxable	£12,500.00		
Basic rate	£12,500.00 x 20%		£2,500.00
Savings Income	£3,500.00		
Personal savings allowance:	£1,000.00 x 0%	£0.00	
Basic rate	£2,500.00 x 20%	£500.00	
	£3,500.00		£500.00
Dividend Income	£6,000.00		
Dividend allowance	£2,000.00 x 0%	£0.00	
Dividend ordinary rate:	£4,000.00 x 7.5%	£300.00	
	£6,000.00		£300.00
Total Income Tax			£3,300.00

3.4

	£	£	£
General Income	60,000.00		
Less personal allowance	12,500.00		
Taxable	47,500.00		
£37,500 x 20%		7,500.00	
£10,000 x 40%		4,000.00	
£47,500			11,500.00
Savings Income	7,500.00		
£500 x 0% (Personal savings allowance)		0.00	
£7,000 x 40%		2,800.00	
£7,500			2,800.00
Dividend Income	5,000.00		
£2,000 x 0% (Dividend allowance)		0.00	
£3,000 x 32.5%		975.00	
£5,000			975.00
Total Income Tax			15,275.00

3.5 (b), (c), (d) and (f) True; (a) and (e) False

Income from employment

4.1

Indicators of Employment	Indicators of Self Employment
Need to do the work yourself	Can employ helper or substitute
Told how, where and when to do work	Decide yourself how, when and where to do work
Work set hours and paid regular wage with sick pay and holidays	Choose work hours and invoice for work done
No risk of capital or losses	Risk own capital and bear losses from work that is not to standard
Employer provides equipment	Provide own equipment
Usually work for one employer	Work for several people or organisations

4.2 **(a)** **(1)** 44 g/km   16%

                (2) 134 g/km   30%

                (3) 151 g/km   34%

                (4) 249 g/km   37%

      (b) **(1)** The cost of the car used in the benefit in kind computation is **£17,000**

                (2) The percentage used in the benefit in kind computation is **37%**

                (3) The assessable benefit for Silvia relating to the car for 2019/20 is **£3,145**

4.3 **(a)** (c)   £75,000

      (b) (a) and (c) Yes; (b) No

      (c) (c)   £9,150   *Workings: (£9,300 + (2.5% x £90,000) – £2,400)*

4.4 £75   *Workings: (£16,000 + £14,000)/2 x 4/12 x (2.5% – 1.0%)*

4.5 **(a)** (b)   She will have a taxable amount of £875

                    Workings: ((10,000 x (50p – 45p)) + (1,500 x (50p – 25p))

      (b) (b)   His taxable salary will be reduced by £1,420

                    Workings: ((£28,400 x 5%, the employer's contribution is tax-free)

      (c) (b)   An allowable deduction of £120. (The net cost to Steve)

      (d) (a)   The employer pays a percentage of her salary into the scheme, but Genna does not

5 Preparing income tax computations

5.1

	£
Employment income	57,500
Rental income	10,350
Savings income	700
Dividend income	6,500
Less Personal Allowance	12,500
Taxable income	62,550
Tax Calculation:	
General income (£57,500 + £10,350 − £12,500) £55,350:	
(£37,500 + £4,000 + £2,000 = £43,500) x 20%	8,700.00
(£55,350 − £43,500) x 40%	4,740.00
Savings income £700:	
Personal savings allowance £500 x 0%	0.00
(£700 − £500 = £200) x 40%	80.00
Dividend income £6,500	
Dividend allowance £2,000 x 0%	0.00
(£6,500 − £2,000 = £4,500) x 32.5%	1,462.50
Tax liability	14,982.50

5.2

Situation	Dave's tax on savings income	Sue's tax on savings income
	£	£
Current position	200	600
All savings in Dave's name	600	0
All savings in Sue's name	0	1,400

5.3

	Normal situation	Replacing carpet and curtains
	£	£
Taxable Income	45,500	39,500
Tax at 20%	7,500	7,500
Tax at 40%	3,200	800
Total Income Tax	10,700	8,300
Net Cost of Replacements		3,600

5.4

Workings:	
	£
Salary	45,000
Car benefit £22,000 x (23% + 9% + 4%)	7,920
Fuel benefit £24,100 x 36%	8,676
Sub total	61,596
Personal allowance	12,500
Taxable income	49,096
Tax at 20%: Band £37,500 + (1,600 x 100/80) = £39,500 x 20%	7,900
Tax at 40%: (£49,096 − £39,500) x 40%	3,838
Total tax liability	11,738

5.5

	£
Employment Income	91,500
Dividends	17,500
	109,000
Personal allowance	8,750
Taxable income	100,250
General income:	
(37,500 + 1,500) x 20%	7,800
(82,750* − 39,000) x 40%	17,500
Dividend income:	
2,000 x 0%	0
15,500 x 32.5%	5,038
Tax liability	30,338

Workings:

Adjusted net income: £91,500 + £17,500 − £1,500 = £107,500

Personal allowance: £12,500 − 50% x (£107,500 − £100,000) = £8,750

*General income: £91,500 − £8,750 = £82,750

6 Capital gains tax

6.1

	Actual proceeds used	Deemed proceeds used	No gain or loss basis
(a) Father gives an asset to his son		✔	
(b) Wife sells an asset to her husband			✔
(c) Simon gives an asset to his friend		✔	
(d) Margaret sells an asset to her cousin for £15,000 when the market value is £40,000	✔		
(e) Brian gives an asset to his civil partner, Dave			✔

6.2 (c) £4,190

True: legal fees are an allowable deduction where they relate to the purchase or sale of an asset.

6.3 (a), (b) and (d) True; (c) False

6.4 **(a)** The gain on the asset is **£12,500**

   (b) The amount of loss that will be relieved is **£500**

   (c) The capital gains tax payable is **£0**

   (d) The loss to be carried forward to the next tax year is **£3,500**

6.5

Asset	Exempt	Chargeable
Antique furniture valued at £30,000		✔
Principal private residence	✔	
Clock	✔	
Shares		✔
Holiday home		✔
Government securities	✔	
Vintage car	✔	
Land		✔

6.6 **(a)**

Occupation / Deemed Occupation	Non-occupation
1/1/2002 - 31/12/2004 (36 months)	
1/1/2005 - 31/12/2005 (12 months)	
1/1/2006 - 30/6/2007 (18 months)	
1/7/2007 - 31/12/2014 (90 months)	1/1/2015 - 30/6/2018 (42 months)
1/7/2018 - 1/1/2020 (18 months)	

(b) Chargeable gain is £**15,556** *Workings: ((£205,000 – £125,000) x 42/216)*

6.7

Asset	Sale proceeds	Cost	Statement
1	£4,000	£7,000	Sale proceeds to be £6,000
2	£14,000	£8,000	Calculate gain as normal
3	£8,000	£3,000	Chattel marginal relief applies
4	£3,000	£5,000	Exempt asset
5	£15,000	£21,000	Calculate loss as normal

6.8

	Number of shares	£
October 2000	20,000	100,000
Bonus	800	0
Sub total	20,800	100,000
Disposal	8,000	38,462
Pool balance	12,800	61,538
Proceeds		72,000
Cost		38,462
Gain		33,538

7 Inheritance tax

7.1   £

Inheritance Tax calculation:

Estate	800,000
Less exempt transfer to Phil	(250,000)
Less exempt transfer to charity	(5,000)
Less residence nil rate band	(150,000)
Less nil rate band	(325,000)
Amount subject to IHT	70,000
Inheritance tax at 40%	28,000

Calculation of amount received by Robert:

Estate	800,000
Less transfer to Phil	(250,000)
Less transfer to charity	(5,000)
Less Inheritance Tax	(28,000)
Balance due to Robert (including home)	517,000

7.2   £

Mary's estate:

Estate	350,000
Less exempt transfer to Paul (£350,000 – £80,000)	(270,000)
Less nil rate band used	(80,000)
Amount subject to IHT	0
Inheritance tax at 40%	0

Paul's estate:

Estate	950,000
Less residence nil rate band (£150,0000 + £150,000)	(300,000)
Less nil rate band (£325,000 + (£325,000 – £80,000))	(570,000)
Chargeable to IHT	80,000
Inheritance Tax at 40%	32,000

7.3

	£	£
Gift to daughter, Rosy	10,000	
Less marriage gift exemption	(5,000)	
		5,000
Less current year annual exemption		(3,000)
Less part of prior year annual exemption		(2,000)
The gift to Rosy does not result in PET		0
Gift to son, Robert		5,000
Less balance of prior year annual exemption		(1,000)
PET resulting from gift to Robert		4,000
PET resulting from gift to parents (no deductions)		2,500

The gifts to charity, the Labour Party, and her husband are all exempt transfers.

7.4 Inheritance Tax due in lifetime:

The chargeable transfer will not result in any IHT payable immediately, since (after deducting two £3,000 annual exemptions) it is £164,000, which is below the £325,000 threshold.

The gift to David is a PET of £20,000, less annual exemption of £3,000 = £17,000. The gift to Masie is a PET of £30,000.

Inheritance tax on death:

	£
Estate	630,000
Less exempt transfer to wife, Julie	(250,000)
Less exempt transfer to charity	(5,000)
Less nil rate band	
(£325,000 − £164,000 − £17,000 − £30,000)	(114,000)
Chargeable to IHT	261,000
Inheritance Tax at 40%	104,400

7.5

	£
Inheritance Tax calculation:	
Estate	800,000
Less exempt transfer to Jim's wife	(200,000)
Less exempt transfer to charity	(100,000)
Less residence nil rate band	(150,000)
Less nil rate band	(325,000)
Amount subject to IHT	25,000
Inheritance tax at 36%*	9,000

*The 'net value' of the estate is (£800,000 − £200,000 − £150,000 − £325,000) = £125,000. The payment to charity of £100,000 is equal to more than 10% of £125,000, and so the rate of 36% applies.

Calculation of amount received by Jim's daughter:

	£
Estate	800,000
Less exempt transfer to Jim's wife	(200,000)
Less exempt transfer to charity	(100,000)
Less Inheritance Tax	(9,000)
Balance due to Jim's daughter (including home)	491,000

Practice
assessment 1

Task 1

You work for a small firm of accountants. One of your clients has arrived for a meeting to review the accounts and tax work that you have completed for his small business. The business's taxable profits are typically about £70,000 per year, and this year's figures show a similar profit.

The client looks at the figures, and then states 'I don't want to provide HMRC with such a high profit figure. I would like to show profits at nearer £50,000 so that I can avoid the higher rate of tax. I don't mind how you adjust the figures – after all it's just a bit of harmless tax avoidance that everyone does.'

Explain how you will deal with this situation.

Task 2

(a) Joe had two company cars during 2019/20 and his employer paid the running costs of each car, including all fuel. The following table shows the details.

Car	Number of months	List price	Price paid	Joe's capital contribution	Scale charge
		£	£	£	%
Ford	4	25,350	25,150	1,000	23
Fiat	8	31,250	22,500	6,500	19

Complete the following table to show Joe's taxable benefit in kind for the cars for 2019/20. Show your answers to the nearest £.

	£
The benefit in kind for the use of the Ford car	
The benefit in kind for the provision of fuel for the Ford car	
The benefit in kind for the use of the Fiat car	
The benefit in kind for the provision of fuel for the Fiat car	

(b) Complete the following table by inserting the scale charge for 2019/20 for each of the cars shown.

	Engine type	CO_2 emissions	Scale charge %
Car 1	Diesel	245	
Car 2	Petrol – electric hybrid	44	

Task 3

The following table shows a list of benefits relating to employment. Enter the assessable amount (or zero for any that are exempt) for each benefit.

	Assessable amount £
Private use of a small van including private fuel from 1 September 2019 until 31 December 2019	
An interest-free loan of £9,000, repayable over 2 years from the loan date of 1 June 2019	
Use of a company flat with an annual value of £5,000. The flat was bought in 2009 for £130,000, and was valued at £200,000 when first occupied by this employee. The flat is not job related	
Use of a home cinema system bought by the employer for £2,000 for the employee's use from 6 June 2019	
A holiday costing £500 was paid for using a company credit card (with the employer's permission)	
A bicycle costing £300 was provided to use both for travelling to work and for leisure	
Free workplace parking in a public car park that costs the employer £2,860 per year	

Task 4

Complete the following sentence for each taxpayer. Enter answers in whole pounds only.

Mabel received a dividend of £7,400. Her other income, before personal allowances was £28,000.

The tax payable on the dividends is £ ⬚

John received £1,650 interest from his bank and £560 interest from his individual savings account. His other taxable income, after the personal allowance was £63,500.

The tax payable on savings income is £ ⬚

Vikram received building society interest of £4,400. His other income was £161,500.

The tax payable on savings income is £ ⬚

Task 5

Complete the following table to show the taxable rent and the allowable expenses for each property. Enter amounts in whole pounds only. All properties are owned by the same individual.

Property	Details	Taxable rent £	Allowable expenses £
10 Major Road	This property was first let on 1 December in the tax year for £800 per month. The tenant paid 6 months' rent in advance, plus a refundable deposit of £1,000. The landlord paid £65 property insurance per month.		
2 Little Lane	This property was let all the tax year for £1,200 per month. The managing agent charged 12% of the rent received. The bathroom fittings were replaced costing £1,500.		
4 Manor Park	This property was occupied by the landlord's son until 30 June in the tax year. The interior was then repainted costing £800 and a tenant moved in on 6 July, paying £900 per month. A washing machine was purchased for the property in July costing £550. There had not been one in the property previously.		

Task 6

(a)   Nigel has the following income for the tax year:

Income from employment	£49,500
Property income	£10,350
Bank interest received	£1,380
Dividends received	£6,400

Nigel has property income losses brought forward of £2,100.

During the tax year, Nigel made gifts to charities under gift-aid of £1,840.

Using the blank table below, calculate Nigel's total income tax liability.

(b)   Gemma has employment income of £49,500, plus bank interest of £950. She has read that interest can be tax-free up to £1,000 per year. Explain to Gemma the rules about how much personal savings allowance individuals are entitled to.

Task 7

During the tax year, Celia received a gross salary of £53,500 and use of a company car with an assessable benefit value of £6,150.

Complete the following table to show the National Insurance Contributions relating to Celia in whole pounds. Ignore the employment allowance.

	£
The total Class 1 NIC payable by Celia in the tax year	
The total Class 1 NIC payable by Celia's employer in the tax year	
The total Class 1A NIC payable by Celia's employer relating to the tax year	

Task 8

(a)   Indicate with ticks whether each of the following statements is true or false.

	True	False
(a) For an interest-free personal loan from an employer to be an exempt benefit the total loan(s) must not exceed £10,000 during the tax year		
(b) A transfer of money to a husband, wife, or civil partner has no implications for either Capital Gains Tax or Inheritance Tax		

(b)   Complete the sentences below.

Dick and Jane are married. They have £60,000 to invest in a savings account that pays 2% interest per year. They have no other savings income. Dick's employment income is £21,000 per year, and Jane's employment income is £63,000 per year.

If the £60,000 is invested in a savings account in Dick's name the tax payable will be

£ [   ] less than if it is invested in Jane's name.

Julie has total income of £110,000 per year. If she pays £4,000 (net) to a charity under gift aid,

her personal allowance will increase by £ [   ]

Rashid will have use of a diesel company car for the whole tax year with a list price of £30,000, and car benefit of 25%. He is a higher-rate taxpayer. If Rashid changes this car to a petrol model with the same list price, but a CO_2 figure 10 g/km lower it would save him

£ [   ] per year in tax (excluding fuel benefit).

Task 9

(a) For each statement, tick the appropriate box.

	Actual proceeds used	Deemed proceeds used	No gain or loss basis
(1) Dave gives an asset to his father			
(2) Peter sells an asset to his friend			
(3) Simon gives an asset to his friend			

(b) John has a capital loss brought forward of £2,500. He has taxable income for the year of £25,000.

He sold an asset during the tax year for £23,000 (not residential property). He had been left the asset when his grandfather died. His grandfather had paid £6,000 for the asset, and it was valued at £9,500 at the time of death.

Complete the following sentences:

(1) The gain on the asset is £ [ ]

(2) The amount of loss that will be relieved is £ [ ]

(3) The capital gains tax payable is £ [ ]

(4) The loss to be carried forward to the next tax year is £ [ ]

(c) Complete the following table to show which assets are exempt from capital gains tax and which are chargeable.

Asset	Exempt	Chargeable
Land		
Principal private residence		
Antique painting valued at £20,000		
Unquoted shares		
Caravan		
Government securities		
Classic car		
Horse		

Task 10

Pam bought 25,000 shares in Lester Ltd for £5 per share in October 2000. In April 2005 she took up a rights issue of 3 for 5 at £4 per share. In January 2020, Pam sold 10,000 shares for £8 per share.

Clearly showing the balance of shares, and their value to carry forward, calculate the gain made on these shares. All workings must be shown in your calculations.

Task 11

The following information is available about four taxpayers who sold capital assets (not residential property) during the tax year. These were their only capital asset disposals. Complete the table to show the capital gains tax payable by each individual, in whole pounds.

Taxpayer	Sold to	Proceeds £	Market value £	Cost £	Other taxable income £	Capital Gains Tax £
Dave	Son	31,500	40,000	25,000	48,000	
Brian	Wife	10,000	50,000	45,000	63,000	
Sue	Friend	15,000	18,000	14,000	21,000	
Alison	Friend	33,000	25,000	13,500	33,000	

Task 12

(a) The following lifetime transfers were made by unconnected individuals. Complete the table to show the value of any potentially exempt transfers, assuming that the annual exempt amounts for the current and previous year have already been utilised. If any transfers are wholly exempt enter a zero.

	Value of PET £
Gill gives Dave £5,000 to celebrate their forthcoming marriage	
Roger donates £10,000 to the National Trust (a registered charity)	
Sue gives her daughter £10,000 to help with a house deposit	

(b) Analyse the following statements about Inheritance Tax into those that are true and those that are false.

	True	False
(a) Individuals that are not domiciled in the UK are always liable for IHT on transfers of their worldwide property		
(b) Individuals that are resident and domiciled in the UK are liable for IHT on transfers of their worldwide property		
(c) A donation to a qualifying political party is an exempt transfer whether made during the individual's lifetime or on death		

Task 13

June and Brian were married. Brian died in 2017, leaving an estate valued at £200,000, having made no lifetime gifts. Brian's estate was not left to June. The estate did not include a home.

June died in 2020, leaving an estate valued at £950,000. Her will stated that £15,000 was to be left to a charity, and the balance of her estate to her only child. June had made no lifetime gifts. The estate included June's home, valued at £400,000

Using the blank table below, calculate the Inheritance Tax payable on June's estate, showing your workings.

Practice assessment 2

Task 1

You work for a small firm of accountants. One of your clients is self employed in the entertainment industry, and an additional rate taxpayer. She has arrived for a meeting that she requested.

She explains that she has been introduced to a 'tax minimisation specialist' who has recommended that she joins a tax avoidance scheme. The scheme involves using various offshore companies which can divert her earnings through a complicated system. She understands that this will save her 'a substantial amount of tax'. She has also been told that HMRC is 'aware of the scheme'.

The client is keen to go ahead, and asks you to explain the differences between tax avoidance and tax evasion, and any implications of joining the scheme.

Give your response in the box below, and note briefly the ethical implications.

Task 2

(a) Miranda had the use of two company cars during the tax year. The company paid for all the running costs of the cars, including all fuel.

Details of the cars are as follows:

Car	Period of use	List price £	Cost £	CO₂ emissions	Type of engine
Ford	5 months of the tax year	28,500	27,600	139 g/km	Petrol
Citroen	7 months of the tax year	29,060	29,000	85 g/km	Diesel

Complete the following table to show Miranda's taxable benefit in kind for the cars for the tax year. Show amounts to the nearest £.

Car		%	£
Ford	Scale charge percentage		
	Taxable benefit on provision of the car		
	Taxable benefit on provision of fuel		
Citroen	Scale charge percentage		
	Taxable benefit on provision of the car		
	Taxable benefit on provision of fuel		
Total taxable benefit			

(b) Complete the following table by inserting the scale charge for 2019/20 for each of the cars shown.

	Engine type	CO₂ emissions	Scale charge %
Car 1	Petrol	185	
Car 2	Electric	0	

Task 3

(a) Indicate whether each of the following will or will not result in an assessable benefit in kind for the employee by ticking the appropriate box.

The following are provided by the employer to the employee	Assessable benefit in kind	Not assessable benefit in kind
(a) Use of a bicycle and helmet to commute to work		
(b) Subscription to gym that is also used by non-employees		
(c) Allowance of £5 per night for incidental costs while staying away from home on business		
(d) Relocation costs of £5,000 when required to move house by the employer		

(b) Robert was provided with the following by his employer during the tax year:

- A new computer games console to use at home for the whole tax year. This cost the employer £350, and remains the employer's property. By the end of the tax year the console was valued at £100.

- An interest free loan of £14,000 at the start of the tax year. Robert repaid £6,000 on 6 January 2020, but made no other repayments.

- Mileage allowance of 60p per mile for business journeys using Robert's own car. Robert claimed for trips totalling 13,000 miles.

Complete the following table to show the total assessable benefits (if any).

	Assessable amount £
Use of computer games console	
Interest free loan	
Mileage allowance	

Task 4

Complete the following sentence for each taxpayer. Enter answers in whole pounds only.

Mary received a dividend of £6,200. Her other income, after the personal allowance was £21,500.

The tax payable on the dividends is £ [   ]

Joe received £650 interest from his bank and £1,560 interest from his individual savings account. His other taxable income, after the personal allowance was £46,500.

The tax payable on savings income is £ [   ]

Alex received dividend income of £4,150. His other income was £152,500.

The tax payable on dividend income is £ [   ]

Task 5

Complete the following table to show the taxable rent and the allowable expenses for each property. Enter amounts in whole pounds only. Rent is normally received on 1st of each month.

Property	Details	Taxable rent £	Allowable expenses £
12 Water Road	This property was let for the whole tax year for £900 per month. The landlord paid £400 per month mortgage interest after taking the restriction into account and £85 per month property insurance. The property flooded in December. The insurance company paid £4,000 out of the £4,500 cost of repairs.		
Upper Lodge	This property was let until 30 June for £1,200 per month. The property was then empty until 1 August, when it was let for the rest of the tax year at £1,250 per month. The managing agent charged 12% of the rent received. The carpets were replaced costing £1,200 during July.		
Manor House	This property was let out until 31 January in the tax year at £1,800 per month. The tenant moved out, owing rent for December and January, and cannot be located. The interior was then repainted costing £1,700 and a new tenant moved in on 6 April. Insurance costs were £60 per month throughout the tax year.		

Task 6

(a) Sadiq has the following income for the tax year:

Income from employment	£51,000
Property income	£6,060
Bank interest received	£780
Dividends received	£5,200

Sadiq has property income losses brought forward of £8,100.

During the tax year, Sadiq made net payments into a personal pension scheme of £2,000.

Using the blank table below, calculate Sadiq's total income tax liability.

(b) Nada has employment income of £48,650, plus bank interest of £3,350. Explain to Nada how the tax on her savings income will be calculated.

Task 7

During the tax year, Donna received a gross salary of £43,900 and benefits in kind with an assessable value of £10,400.

Complete the following table to show the National Insurance Contributions relating to Donna in whole pounds. Ignore the employment allowance.

	£
The total Class 1 NIC payable by Donna in the tax year	
The total Class 1 NIC payable by Donna's employer in the tax year	
The total Class 1A NIC payable by Donna's employer relating to the tax year	

Task 8

(a) Indicate with ticks whether each of the following statements is true or false.

	True	False
(a) For a personal loan from an employer to be an assessable benefit the total loan(s) must exceed £10,000 during the tax year and the interest rate must be lower than the official rate		
(b) When an individual transfers their cash ISA to a different provider they lose the tax free status of the interest for the current tax year		

(b) Complete the sentences below.

Paul and Cath are married. They are considering buying 20,000 shares in a company that consistently pays dividends of 40 pence per share each year. Paul's employment income is £32,000 per year, and Cath's employment income is £58,000 per year. They have no other income.

If the shares are bought in Paul's name the tax payable on the dividends will be

£ [   ] less than if they are bought in Cath's name.

Joan has total income of £110,000 per year, including provisional property income of £20,000.

If Joan spends an extra £3,000 replacing a carpet in a rental property she will save tax of

£ [   ]

Roger will have use of a diesel company car for the whole tax year, together with free fuel. The car benefit is 35%. He is a higher-rate taxpayer. If Roger changes this car to a petrol model with a CO_2 figure 35 g/km lower it would save him annual tax on just the fuel benefit of

£ [   ] to the nearest £.

Task 9

(a)   Indicate whether each of the following statements is true or false.

	True	False
(a) A chattel bought and sold for less than £6,000 is exempt from capital gains tax		
(b) Transfers between spouses are carried out on a 'no gain, no loss' basis		
(c) Capital gains tax will be incurred on the increase in value of investments between the date of purchase and the date of the owners' death		
(d) Mechanical chattels (for example clocks) owned for personal use are exempt from capital gains tax		

(b)   Josie bought a painting for £14,000 and spent £3,000 having it restored and £800 insuring it. She sold it for £16,000.

Select the capital gain or loss on disposal from the following:

(a)	Zero (exempt asset)	
(b)	Gain of £2,000	
(c)	Loss of £1,000	
(d)	Loss of £1,800	

(c)   Jack's grandfather, John, bought an asset for £6,600. Some years later John died and left the asset to Jack in his will. The asset was valued at £9,400 at that time.

Recently, Jack sold the asset to his sister, Jill, for £6,000 when it was valued at £11,000.

Complete the following table to calculate the gain or loss when Jack sold the asset to Jill. Use a minus sign to denote a loss.

	£
Proceeds or deemed proceeds	
Cost or deemed cost	
Gain or loss	

Task 10

Ken bought 800 shares in Kandle Ltd for £3,000 in April 2003. In May 2009 he bought a further 1,200 shares for £3.90 each. In December 2010 a rights issue of 1 for 5 at £2.00 per share was offered, and Ken took up the offer.

Ken sold 500 shares on 11 November 2019 for a total of £3,000. On 23 December 2019 he purchased a further 100 shares for £6.30 each.

Clearly showing the balance of shares and their value to carry forward, calculate the gain made on the sale of shares that occurred in 2019/20.

Task 11

The following information is available about four taxpayers who sold capital assets (not residential property) during the tax year. These were their only capital asset disposals. Complete the table to show the capital gains tax payable by each individual, in whole pounds.

Taxpayer	Sold to	Proceeds	Market value	Cost	Other taxable income	Capital Gains Tax
		£	£	£	£	£
Adam	Cousin	41,500	50,000	29,000	58,000	
Ben	Wife	35,000	40,000	20,000	23,000	
Chloe	Stranger	25,000	28,000	12,000	21,000	
Della	Friend	23,000	35,000	10,500	31,000	

Task 12

(a) The following lifetime transfers were the only gifts made in the tax year by unconnected individuals. Complete the table to show the value of any potentially exempt transfers, assuming that the annual exempt amounts for the current and previous year have not been utilised. If any transfers are wholly exempt enter a zero.

	Value of PET
	£
Sue gives her daughter £12,000 to celebrate her marriage	
Roger donates £20,000 to a qualifying political party	
Richard gives his son £25,000 to help with a house deposit	

(b) Analyse the following statements about Inheritance Tax into those that are true and those that are false.

	True	False
(a) The annual allowance of £3,000 can be used as a deduction from a death estate		
(b) Taper relief can reduce the tax rate at death where lifetime transfers were made between three and seven years before death		
(c) When any amount is bequeathed to charity at death, the tax rate on the chargeable part of the estate is reduced to 36%		

Task 13

The only lifetime transfer made by Helen was a PET of £400,000 (after exemptions) made on 31 December 2013.

Helen died on 31 January 2020, leaving an estate valued at £50,000 to her son. The estate did not include a home.

Using the blank table below, calculate the Inheritance Tax payable due to Helen's death, showing your workings.

Practice
assessment 3

Task 1

You work for a small firm of accountants. One of your clients for accounts and tax work owns a business that acts as a wholesaler of DIY products. You are concerned about several large receipts and payments through the business bank account that do not appear to have any documentation.

The client has been asked what the transactions relate to. He has explained that all the transactions relate to his brother-in-law's restaurant business. 'He needed to reduce his cash balance for some reason. I said that he could put some money in my account and that I would invoice him later on for something. When he wanted the money back we could call it 'management charges' or something. We haven't got around to doing the paperwork yet. Maybe you can help with this.'

Explain in the box below how the situation should be dealt with.

Task 2

(a) Dirk is a senior manager in the defence industry. During the tax year he was provided with the following company cars:

From the start of the tax year until 30 June he was provided with a Jaguar. It was purchased for £41,000 second hand, and had a list price of £52,000. Its emissions were 152 g/km and it was powered by a petrol engine.

Following a promotion for Dirk, the Jaguar was replaced with a new diesel powered Range Rover on 1 July. This car had a list price of £72,000. The company believed that Dirk's new role placed him at increased risk of a terrorism attack, and paid £25,000 for the Range Rover to be equipped with bullet resistant glass and strengthened bodywork. The emissions of the car were 230 g/km. On 1 December the car was fitted with passengers' televisions so that Dirk's family could be entertained on long trips. This cost the company £1,200.

Complete the following table to show the benefit in kind arising from the use of these cars. Ignore any benefit arising from private fuel.

Car	Percentage applicable based on CO$_2$ emissions %	Cost of car used in benefit calculation £	Benefit in kind £
Jaguar			
Range Rover			
Total			

(b) Complete the following table by inserting the scale charge for 2019/20 for each of the cars shown.

	Engine type	CO$_2$ emissions	Scale charge %
Car 1	Diesel	142	
Car 2	Petrol	158	

Task 3

(a) Place a tick in the appropriate column of the table below to show whether each of the items listed would or would not result in an assessable benefit in kind for an employee.

The following are provided by the employer to the employee	Benefit in kind	No benefit in kind
(a) Use of a company credit card to pay for the entertainment of customers (with approval of the employer)		
(b) Mileage payment for use of employee's own motorcycle for business purposes at a rate of 24p per mile		
(c) Petrol for travel from home to work in a company car		
(d) Training costs including course and examination fees for accountancy trainee undertaking AAT course		

(b) Calculate the assessable benefit in kind (in whole pounds) for each of the following:

	Benefit £
On 6 April an employee was provided with an interest free loan of £15,000. During the tax year he made three repayments, each of £2,000. The remainder of the loan was still outstanding at the end of the tax year.	
On 6 April an employee was allowed the use of a home cinema system that had previously been used by the company. The home cinema had originally cost the company £1,500, but its market value on 6 April was £1,000.	

(c)   Using the following table, analyse the benefits into those that are exempt from tax, and those that are taxable.

Description	Exempt	Taxable
Provision of a chauffeur for business and private journeys		
Long service award in cash for employee with 10 years' service		
Counselling services		
Free meals in a staff restaurant available to all staff		
Provision of free UK health insurance		

(d)   Tick the appropriate box to show whether each of the following situations would increase or reduce an employee's tax liability under the approved mileage allowance payments scheme.

Business mileage and rate paid	Increase tax liability	Reduce tax liability
5,000 miles at 50p per mile		
15,000 miles at 45p per mile		
15,000 miles at 38p per mile		
20,000 miles at 25p per mile		

Task 4

Complete the following sentence for each taxpayer. Enter answers in whole pounds only.

Monica received a dividend of £6,000. Her other income was £151,500.

The tax payable on the dividends is £ ⬚

Jonathan received £2,650 interest from his bank. His only other income was employment income of £24,000.

The tax payable on savings income is £ ⬚

Alan received dividend income of £6,200. His other income, before the personal allowance, was £52,500.

The tax payable on dividend income is £ ⬚

Task 5

Complete the following table to show the taxable rent and the allowable expenses (or property allowance if applicable) for each property. Enter amounts in whole pounds only. Each property is let by a separate individual landlord.

Property	Details	Taxable rent £	Allowable expenses/ Property allowance £
1 Henry Road	This property was let for the whole tax year for £950 per month. The landlord paid £40 per month property insurance. During the year, the landlord installed central heating where none existed previously, costing £6,000. The mortgage interest (after applying the restriction) was £6,000 for the year.		
Middle House	This property was let until 5 October for £1,000 per month. The property was then used as a second home by the landlord. The buildings insurance was £20 per month.		
3 Lincoln Road	This property was let out until 5 February in the tax year at £800 per month. The interior was then decorated costing £1,200 and the carpets were replaced costing £1,800. A new tenant moved in on 6 March paying £820 per month.		

Task 6

(a)   Sarah has the following income for the tax year:

Income from employment   £45,000

Property income   £8,150

Bank interest received   £1,780

Dividends received   £4,200

During the tax year, Sarah made net payments into a personal pension scheme of £800.

Using the blank table below, calculate Sarah's total income tax liability.

(b) Nadia has employment income of £49,000, plus dividend income of £4,500. Explain to Nadia how the tax on her dividend income will be calculated.

Task 7

During the tax year, Ellen received a gross salary of £9,000 and benefits in kind with an assessable value of £400.

Complete the following table to show the National Insurance Contributions relating to Ellen in whole pounds. Ignore the employment allowance.

	£
The total Class 1 NIC payable by Ellen in the tax year	
The total Class 1 NIC payable by Ellen's employer in the tax year	
The total Class 1A NIC payable by Ellen's employer relating to the tax year	

Task 8

(a) Indicate with ticks whether each of the following statements is true or false.

	True	False
(a) If a wholly electric car is provided as a company car the benefit percentage will be 16% for use of the car and any electricity charging provided by the employer will be tax free		
(b) Individuals aged 18 or over can move their investment from a cash ISA to a stocks and shares ISA without any restrictions		

(b) Complete the sentences below.

Peter is a basic rate taxpayer in the current year, but will be a higher rate taxpayer next year. He currently has no savings income, but has recently been given £50,000 from his late uncle's estate. He is considering a one year savings account that has two options for receiving interest. A monthly interest option would give him interest of £400 this tax year and £600 next tax year. An annual interest option would mean that he receives £1,000 next tax year.

If the monthly interest option is chosen, then over the two tax years Peter will pay

£ [   ] less tax on savings income than if the annual interest option is chosen.

Jo has total income of £106,000 per year. If Jo earned a further £1,000 as an employment bonus

her tax would increase by £ [   ]

Roland is a basic rate taxpayer. His employer has offered a scheme in which Roland's pay would reduce by £40 per week, but the company would increase their pension contributions by the same amount.

In a full tax year, this would save Roland Income Tax of £ [   ]

Task 9

(a) A taxpayer had previously bought an asset for £14,000, plus 6% auction commission. He sold it during the tax year for £15,000, having spent £100 to advertise it for sale. The cost of insuring the asset during his ownership was £150.

Calculate the gain or loss using the following computation.

	Amount £
Proceeds	
Total costs	
Gain / Loss	

(b) Complete the following table to show which statements are true and which are false in connection with capital gains tax.

Statement	True	False
(a) Gifts to charities are exempt from capital gains tax		
(b) Gifts between a father and son are exempt from capital gains tax		
(c) When applying the 5/3 restriction to chattels, the proceeds figure used is before any costs of sale are deducted		
(d) Chattels are defined as tangible moveable property		
(e) Non-wasting chattels are exempt from capital gains tax		

(c) Complete the following sentences.

A taxpayer had capital losses brought forward of £6,000. During the tax year he made two disposals, making a gain of £16,300 on one and a loss of £1,900 on the other.

The amount subject to capital gains tax for the year (after the annual exempt amount) will be:

£ [   ]

The capital loss to be carried forward to be set against future gains will be:

£ [   ]

Task 10

Paul bought 18,000 shares in Leicester Ltd for £4.50 per share in October 2000. In April 2012 he took up a rights issue of 4 for 9 at £3 per share. In January 2020, Paul sold 12,000 shares for £6 per share.

Clearly showing the balance of shares, and their value to carry forward, calculate the gain made on these shares. All workings must be shown in your calculations.

Task 11

The following information is available about four taxpayers who sold capital assets (not residential property) during the tax year. These were their only capital asset disposals. Complete the table to show the capital gains tax payable by each individual, in whole pounds.

Taxpayer	Sold to	Proceeds	Market value	Cost	Other taxable income	Capital Gains Tax
		£	£	£	£	£
Ella	Grandfather	48,500	55,000	24,000	58,000	
Fred	Civil Partner	29,000	40,000	12,000	20,000	
Gareth	Stranger	25,000	20,000	10,000	22,000	
Helen	Friend	20,000	32,000	8,500	45,000	

Task 12

(a) The following lifetime transfers were the only gifts made in the tax year by unconnected individuals. Complete the table to show the value of any potentially exempt transfers, assuming that the annual exempt amounts for the current and previous year have not been utilised. If any transfers are wholly exempt enter a zero.

	Value of PET
	£
Stan gives his son £15,000 to celebrate his marriage	
Ron donates £2,000 to a museum	
Robert gives his nephew £15,000 to help with a house deposit	

(b) Analyse the following statements about Inheritance Tax into those that are true and those that are false.

	True	False
(a) The annual allowance of £3,000 can only be carried forward for one tax year		
(b) Taper relief can reduce the tax rate at death where lifetime transfers were made between zero and three years before death		
(c) When more than 10% of the net value of an estate is bequeathed to charity at death, the tax rate on the chargeable part of the estate is reduced to 36%		

Task 13

The only lifetime transfer made by Ivor was a chargeable transfer to a trust of £100,000 (after exemptions) made on 31 December 2015.

Ivor died on 31 January 2020, leaving an estate valued at £450,000 to his son, including a home worth £200,000.

Using the blank table below, calculate any Inheritance Tax payable during Ivor's lifetime and on Ivor's death, showing your workings.

Answers to practice assessment 1

Task 1

The accounts and tax work that has already been undertaken should be reviewed with the client to ensure that all allowances have been accounted for in the most tax-efficient manner. This is normal tax minimisation.

What the client is proposing is illegal tax evasion, not legal tax avoidance. The suggestion is that the accounts are manipulated to reduce the amount of tax that appears to be due. Tax evasion is a criminal activity.

The AAT Code of Professional Ethics makes it clear that accountancy and tax work must be carried out with professional competence and be consistent with the law. To 'adjust' the figures in the way suggested would not be consistent with the law, and must not be carried out.

Although the client would bear ultimate responsibility for submissions made to HMRC, we cannot be associated with any submission that we believe contains inaccuracies.

The client should be asked to reconsider his request that we alter the figures, and asked to agree to submit the original data. If he refuses then we should cease to act for him.

We would then inform HMRC that we no longer act for the client. The reason for ceasing to act would not normally be given to HMRC, as this would be a breach of confidentiality. There appears to be no suggestion here of money laundering which could override the rules regarding confidentiality.

Task 2

(a)

	£
The benefit in kind for the use of the Ford car	1,867
The benefit in kind for the provision of fuel for the Ford car	1,848
The benefit in kind for the use of the Fiat car	3,325
The benefit in kind for the provision of fuel for the Fiat car	3,053

(b)

	Engine type	CO_2 emissions	Scale charge %
Car 1	Diesel	245	37
Car 2	Petrol – electric hybrid	44	16

Task 3

	Assessable amount £
Private use of a small van including private fuel from 1 September 2019 until 31 December 2019	1,362
An interest-free loan of £9,000, repayable over 2 years from the loan date of 1 June 2019	0
Use of a company flat with an annual value of £5,000. The flat was bought in 2009 for £130,000, and was valued at £200,000 when first occupied by this employee. The flat is not job related	8,125
Use of a home cinema system bought by the employer for £2,000 for the employee's use from 6 June 2019	333
A holiday costing £500 was paid for using a company credit card (with the employer's permission)	500
A bicycle costing £300 was provided to use both for travelling to work and for leisure	0
Free workplace parking in a public car park that costs the employer £2,860 per year	0

Task 4

The tax payable on the dividends is £**405**

The tax payable on savings income is £**460**

The tax payable on savings income is £**1,980**

Task 5

Property	Taxable rent £	Allowable expenses £
10 Major Road	4,800	260
2 Little Lane	14,400	3,228
4 Manor Park	8,100	800

Task 6

(a)

	Workings	£
Employment income		49,500
Property income	£10,350 – £2,100	8,250
Savings income		1,380
Dividend income		6,400
Less personal allowance		12,500
Taxable income		53,030
General income £45,250	£49,500 + £8,250 – £12,500	
Tax on general income:	(£37,500 + (£1,840/0.8)) x 20%	7,960
	£5,450 x 40%	2,180
Tax on savings income:	£500 x 0%	0
	£880 x 40%	352
Tax on dividend income:	£2,000 x 0%	0
	£4,400 x 32.5%	1,430
Tax liability		11,922

(b)   Savings income (eg bank interest) is tax-free for basic rate taxpayers up to £1,000 per year. For higher rate taxpayers like Gemma the tax-free amount is up to £500, so the remaining £450 would be taxable (at the higher rate). Additional rate taxpayers are not entitled to any personal savings allowance.

Although the savings income covered by the personal savings allowance is tax free, it still counts within the band, so can push dividend income into the next band.

Task 7

	£
The total Class 1 NIC payable by Celia in the tax year	5,034
The total Class 1 NIC payable by Celia's employer in the tax year	6,191
The total Class 1A NIC payable by Celia's employer relating to the tax year	848

Task 8

(a) Both are True

(b) If the £60,000 is invested in a savings account in Dick's name the tax payable will be **£240** less than if it is invested in Jane's name.

Julie has total income of £110,000 per year. If she pays £4,000 (net) to a charity under gift aid, her personal allowance will increase by **£2,500**.

If Rashid changes this car to a petrol model with the same list price, but a CO_2 figure 10 g/km lower it would save him **£720** per year in tax (excluding fuel benefit).

Task 9

(a)

	Actual proceeds used	Deemed proceeds used	No gain or loss basis
(1) Dave gives an asset to his father		✔	
(2) Peter sells an asset to his friend	✔		
(3) Simon gives an asset to his friend		✔	

(b) **(1)** The gain on the asset is **£13,500**

(2) The amount of loss that will be relieved is **£1,500**

(3) The capital gains tax payable is **£0**

(4) The loss to be carried forward to the next tax year is **£1,000**

(c)

Asset	Exempt	Chargeable
Land		✔
Principal private residence	✔	
Antique painting valued at £20,000		✔
Unquoted shares		✔
Caravan	✔	
Government securities	✔	
Classic car	✔	
Horse	✔	

Task 10

	Number of Shares	Value £
Purchase	25,000	125,000
Rights	15,000	60,000
Sub total	40,000	185,000
Disposal	10,000	46,250
Balance	30,000	138,750
Proceeds		80,000
Cost		46,250
Gain		33,750

Task 11

Taxpayer	Sold to	Proceeds	Market value	Cost	Other taxable income	Capital Gains Tax
		£	£	£	£	£
Dave	Son	31,500	40,000	25,000	48,000	600
Brian	Wife	10,000	50,000	45,000	63,000	0
Sue	Friend	15,000	18,000	14,000	21,000	0
Alison	Friend	33,000	25,000	13,500	33,000	1,050

Task 12

(a)

	Value of PET
	£
Gill gives Dave £5,000 to celebrate their forthcoming marriage	2,500
Roger donates £10,000 to the National Trust (a registered charity)	0
Sue gives her daughter £10,000 to help with a house deposit	10,000

(b) (a) False; (b) and (c) True

Task 13

	Workings / Notes	£
June's estate		950,000
Less exempt transfer	Charity (under 10% net estate)	15,000
Less residence nil rate band	£150,000 + £150,000	300,000
Less nil rate band		325,000
Less Brian's unused band	£325,000 − £200,000	125,000
Taxable		185,000
Inheritance Tax	£185,000 x 40%	74,000

Answers to practice assessment 2

Task 1

Tax avoidance is the legal use of claims and allowances to reduce the amount of tax payable. Tax evasion involves using illegal methods to reduce tax. There is a grey area between these two activities, and it is not always clear how HMRC or the courts will define a particular activity or scheme.

Where a scheme relies on concealment, pretence, non-disclosure or misrepresentation, this would be categorised as tax evasion which can result in criminal prosecution.

'Aggressive' tax avoidance schemes may also be examined under the General Anti-Abuse Rule (GAAR) legislation which will consider whether the law is being used in the way that Parliament originally anticipated.

If HMRC are aware of a particular scheme it does not mean that they have approved it as being legal. There could be ongoing investigations into the scheme which could result in it being declared illegal. Taxpayers must disclose their use of avoidance schemes, and will consequently be viewed as high risk individuals by HMRC. Their tax affairs may be subject to more scrutiny as a result.

Accountants should also consider their own ethical position when clients wish to undertake tax avoidance, and distance themselves from situations that do not meet their own or their professional body's ethical standards. They must also consider any reputational damage that may occur as a result of facilitating their clients' involvement in particular schemes.

Task 2

(a)

Car		%	£
Ford	Scale charge percentage	31	
	Taxable benefit on provision of the car		3,681
	Taxable benefit on provision of fuel		3,113
Citroen	Scale charge percentage	26	
	Taxable benefit on provision of the car		4,407
	Taxable benefit on provision of fuel		3,655
Total taxable benefit			14,856

(b)

	Engine type	CO_2 emissions	Scale charge %
Car 1	Petrol	185	37
Car 2	Electric	0	16

Task 3

(a) **(b)** will result in an assessable benefit in kind; the other options will NOT.

(b)

	Assessable amount £
Use of computer games console	70
Interest free loan	275
Mileage allowance	2,550

Task 4

The tax payable on the dividends is £**315**

The tax payable on savings income is £**60**

The tax payable on dividend income is £**819**

Task 5

Property	Taxable rent £	Allowable expenses £
12 Water Road	10,800	6,320
Upper Lodge	13,650	2,838
Manor House	12,600	2,420

Task 6

(a)

	Workings	£
Employment Income		51,000
Property Income	£6,060 – £8,100 = –£2,040 cf	0
Savings Income		780
Dividend Income		5,200
Less personal allowance		12,500
		44,480
General Income	£51,000 – £12,500 = £38,500	
Basic rate tax	£38,500 x 20%	7,700
Savings Income	£500 x 0% PSA	0
	£280 x 20%	56
Dividend Income*	£2,000 x 0% DA	0
	£3,200 x 32.5%	1,040
Tax liability		8,796

*Note – the revised top of the basic rate band is £40,000. This occurs within the dividend allowance.

(b) Nada's total income after deducting the personal allowance is £48,650 + £3,350 – £12,500 = £39,500. As this exceeds the band limit of £37,500, she will be a higher rate taxpayer, and entitled to £500 personal savings allowance. This allowance will use up some of the basic rate band as the following calculations will show.

General income (from employment) is (£48,650 – £12,500) = £36,150, and this is taxed at basic rate.

The savings income will be taxed as follows:

£500 x 0% (personal savings allowance)	=	£0.00
£850 x 20% (basic rate to £37,500 cumulative)	=	£170.00
£2,000 x 40% (higher rate)	=	£800.00
Total tax on savings income		£970.00

Task 7

	£
The total Class 1 NIC payable by Donna in the tax year	4,232
The total Class 1 NIC payable by Donna's employer in the tax year	4,866
The total Class 1A NIC payable by Donna's employer relating to the tax year	1,435

Task 8

(a)   (a) True; (b) False

(b)   If the shares are bought in Paul's name the tax payable on the dividends will be £**1,500** less than if they are bought in Cath's name.

If Joan spends an extra £3,000 replacing a carpet in a rental property she will save tax of £**1,800**.

If Roger changes this car to a petrol model with a CO_2 figure 35 g/km lower it would save him annual tax on just the fuel benefit of £**1,060**.

Task 9

(a)   (a), (b) and (d) True; (c) False

(b)   (c)   Loss of £1,000

(c)

	£
Proceeds or deemed proceeds	11,000
Cost or deemed cost	9,400
Gain or loss	1,600

Task 10

		Number of shares	Value £
April 2003	Purchase	800	3,000
May 2009	Purchase	1,200	4,680
December 2010	Rights issue	400	800
		2,400	8,480
November 2019	Disposal	500	1,767
	Balance	1,900	6,713
December 2019	Purchase	100	630
	Balance	2,000	7,343
		£	
	Proceeds	3,000	
	Cost	1,767	
	Gain	1,233	

Task 11

Taxpayer	Sold to	Proceeds	Market value	Cost	Other taxable income	Capital Gains Tax
		£	£	£	£	£
Adam	Cousin	41,500	50,000	29,000	58,000	100
Ben	Wife	35,000	40,000	20,000	23,000	0
Chloe	Stranger	25,000	28,000	12,000	21,000	100
Della	Friend	23,000	35,000	10,500	31,000	50

Task 12

(a)

	Value of PET
	£
Sue gives her daughter £12,000 to celebrate her marriage	1,000
Roger donates £20,000 to a qualifying political party	0
Richard gives his son £25,000 to help with a house deposit	19,000

(b) (b) True; (a) and (c) False

Task 13

	Workings / Notes	£
PET now chargeable	6 to 7 years before death	400,000
Less nil rate band		325,000
Chargeable to IHT		75,000
IHT due on PET (by recipient)	£75,000 x 40% x 20%	6,000
Death estate		50,000
Less nil rate band remaining		0
Chargeable to IHT		50,000
IHT due on estate (by son)	£50,000 x 40%	20,000
Total IHT due	£6,000 + £20,000	£26,000

Answers to practice assessment 3

Task 1

It appears that the client is proposing the accounts are falsified to deal with the transactions with his brother-in-law's business. It is also possible that there could be money laundering involved.

The accountancy practice should certainly not become involved with assisting in the creation of fictitious documents or record any transactions in a way that is known to be false.

Advice should be sought from a more senior person within the practice about the best way to proceed. If money laundering is suspected then the normal rules of client confidentiality do not apply and the matter should be reported to the National Crime Agency without alerting the client.

If money laundering is not suspected then the client should be informed that the transactions must be recorded accurately. If the client will not accept this treatment of the transactions, then the practice should cease to act for the client.

Task 2

(a)

Car	Percentage applicable based on CO_2 emissions %	Cost of car used in benefit calculation £	Benefit in kind £
Jaguar	34	52,000	4,420
Range Rover	37	73,200	20,313
Total			24,733

(b)

	Engine type	CO_2 emissions	Scale charge %
Car 1	Diesel	142	36
Car 2	Petrol	158	35

Task 3

(a) (c) will result in an assessable benefit in kind; the other options will NOT.

(b)

	Benefit £
On 6 April an employee was provided with an interest free loan of £15,000. During the tax year he made three repayments, each of £2,000. The remainder of the loan was still outstanding at the end of the tax year.	300
On 6 April an employee was allowed the use of a home cinema system that had previously been used by the company. The home cinema had originally cost the company £1,500, but its market value on 6 April was £1,000.	200

(c)

Description	Exempt	Taxable
Provision of a chauffeur for business and private journeys		✔
Long service award in cash for employee with 10 years' service		✔
Counselling services	✔	
Free meals in a staff restaurant available to all staff	✔	
Provision of free UK health insurance		✔

(d)

Business mileage and rate paid	Increase tax liability	Reduce tax liability
5,000 miles at 50p per mile	✔	
15,000 miles at 45p per mile	✔	
15,000 miles at 38p per mile		✔
20,000 miles at 25p per mile		✔

Task 4

The tax payable on the dividends is £**1,524**

The tax payable on savings income is £**330**

The tax payable on dividend income is £**1,365**

Task 5

Property	Taxable rent £	Allowable expenses/ Property allowance £
1 Henry Road	11,400	6,480
Middle House	6,000	1,000
3 Lincoln Road	8,820	3,000

Task 6

(a)

	Workings	£
Employment Income		45,000
Property Income		8,150
Savings Income		1,780
Dividend Income		4,200
Less Personal Allowance		12,500
		46,630
General Income £40,650	£45,000 + £8,150 − £12,500	
Basic rate tax	(£37,500 + £1,000) x 20%	7,700
Higher rate	(£40,650 − £38,500) x 40%	860
Savings Income £1,780	£500 x 0% PSA	0
	(£1,780 − £500) x 40%	512
Dividend Income £4,200	£2,000 x 0% DA	0
	£2,200 x 32.5%	715
Tax liability		9,787

(b)   Nadia will be entitled to the dividend allowance that means the first £2,000 of her dividend income will be taxed at 0%. This income still counts within the bands, so this pushes all her remaining dividend of £2,500 into the dividend upper rate band. This is because £49,000 + £2,000 − £12,500 personal allowance = £38,500 which exceeds the £37,500 basic rate band. The remaining £2,500 dividend income will therefore be taxed at 32.5% = £812.50 tax.

Task 7

	£
The total Class 1 NIC payable by Ellen in the tax year	44
The total Class 1 NIC payable by Ellen's employer in the tax year	50
The total Class 1A NIC payable by Ellen's employer relating to the tax year	55

Task 8

(a) Both statements are True

(b) If the monthly interest option is chosen, then over the two tax years Peter will pay **£160** less tax on savings income than if the annual interest option is chosen.

If Jo earned a further £1,000 as an employment bonus her tax would increase by **£600**.

In a full tax year, this would save Roland Income Tax of **£416**.

Task 9

(a)

	Amount £
Proceeds	15,000
Total costs	14,940
Gain	60

(b) (a), (c) and (d) True; (b) and (e) False

(c) The amount subject to capital gains tax for the year (after the annual exempt amount) will be **£0**.

The capital loss to be carried forward to be set against future gains will be **£3,600**.

Task 10

October 2000	18,000	£81,000
April 2012	8,000	£24,000
	26,000	£105,000
Disposal	12,000	£48,462
Pool balance	14,000	£56,538
Proceeds		£72,000
Cost		£48,462
Gain		£23,538

Task 11

Taxpayer	Sold to	Proceeds £	Market value £	Cost £	Other taxable income £	Capital Gains Tax £
Ella	Grandfather	48,500	55,000	24,000	58,000	3,800
Fred	Civil Partner	29,000	40,000	12,000	20,000	0
Gareth	Stranger	25,000	20,000	10,000	22,000	300
Helen	Friend	20,000	32,000	8,500	45,000	0

Task 12

(a)

	Value of PET £
Stan gives his son £15,000 to celebrate his marriage	4,000
Ron donates £2,000 to a museum	0
Robert gives his nephew £15,000 to help with a house deposit	9,000

(b)   (a) and (c) True; (b) False

Task 13

	Workings / Notes	£
Tax payable during lifetime	No tax as transfer below nil band	0
Tax calculation on death		
Estate		450,000
Less Residence Nil Rate Band		150,000
Less nil rate band	£325,000 – £100,000	225,000
Chargeable to IHT		75,000
Inheritance Tax	£75,000 x 40%	30,000

Reference Material

for AAT Assessment of Personal Tax

Finance Act 2019

Professional conduct in relation to taxation

For assessments from 1 January – 31 December 2020

Note: this reference material is accessible by candidates during their live computer based assessment for Personal Tax.

This material was current at the time this book was published, but may be subject to change. Readers are advised to check the AAT website or Osborne Books website for any updates.

Reference material for AAT assessment of Personal Tax

Introduction

This document comprises data that you may need to consult during your Personal Tax computer-based assessment. The material can be consulted during the practice and live assessments through pop-up windows. It is made available here so you can familiarise yourself with the content before the test.

Do not take a print of this document into the exam room with you. Unless you need a printed version as part of reasonable adjustments for particular needs, in which case you must discuss this with your tutor at least six weeks before the assessment date.

This document may be changed to reflect periodical updates in the computer-based assessment, so please check you have the most recent version while studying. This version is based on Finance Act 2019 and is for use in AAT assessments 1 January – 31 December 2020.

> **Note: Page numbers are those of the original AAT Reference Document**

Contents

1. Interpretation and abbreviations

Context

Tax advisors operate in a complex business and financial environment. The increasing public focus on the role of taxation in wider society means a greater interest in the actions of tax advisors and their clients.

This guidance, written by the professional bodies for their members working in tax, sets out the hallmarks of a good tax advisor, and in particular the fundamental principles of behaviour that members are expected to follow.

Interpretation

1.1   In this guidance:
- 'Client' includes, where the context requires, 'former client'.
- 'Member' (and 'members') includes 'firm' or 'practice' and the staff thereof.
- Words in the singular include the plural and words in the plural include the singular.

Abbreviations

1.2   The following abbreviations have been used:

AML	Anti-Money Laundering
CCAB	Consultative Committee of Accountancy Bodies
DOTAS	Disclosure of Tax Avoidance Schemes
GAAP	Generally Accepted Accounting Principles
GAAR	General Anti-Abuse Rule in Finance Act 2013
GDPR	General Data Protection Regulation
HMRC	Her Majesty's Revenue and Customs
MTD	Making Tax Digital
MLRO	Money Laundering Reporting Officer
NCA	National Crime Agency (previously the Serious Organised Crime Agency, SOCA)
POTAS	Promoters of Tax Avoidance Schemes
PCRT	Professional Conduct in Relation to Taxation
SRN	Scheme Reference Number

2.   Fundamental principles

Overview of the fundamental principles

1.   Ethical behaviour in the tax profession is critical. The work carried out by a member needs to be trusted by society at large as well as by clients and other stakeholders. What a member does reflects not just on themselves but on the profession as a whole.

2.   A member must comply with the following fundamental principles:

Integrity
To be straightforward and honest in all professional and business relationships.

Objectivity
To not allow bias, conflict of interest or undue influence of others to override professional or business judgements.

Professional competence and due care
To maintain professional knowledge and skill at the level required to ensure that a client or employer receives competent professional service based on current developments in practice, legislation and techniques and act diligently and in accordance with applicable technical and professional standards.

Confidentiality
To respect the confidentiality of information acquired as a result of professional and business relationships and, therefore, not disclose any such information to third parties without proper and specific authority, unless there is a legal or professional right or duty to disclose, nor use the information for the personal advantage of the member or third parties.

Professional behaviour
To comply with relevant laws and regulations and avoid any action that discredits the profession.

3. PCRT Help sheet A: Submission of tax information and 'Tax filings'

Definition of filing of tax information and tax filings (filing)

1. For the purposes of this guidance, the term 'filing' includes any online submission of data, online filing or other filing that is prepared on behalf of the client for the purposes of disclosing to any taxing authority details that are to be used in the calculation of tax due by a client or a refund of tax due to the client or for other official purposes. It includes all taxes, NIC and duties.

2. A letter, or online notification, giving details in respect of a filing or as an amendment to a filing including, for example, any voluntary disclosure of an error should be dealt with as if it was a filing.

Making Tax Digital and filing

3. Tax administration systems, including the UK's, are increasingly moving to mandatory digital filing of tax information and returns.

4. Except in exceptional circumstances, a member will explicitly file in their capacity as agent. A member is advised to use the facilities provided for agents and to avoid knowing or using the client's personal access credentials.

5. A member should keep their access credentials safe from unauthorised use and consider periodic change of passwords.

6. A member is recommended to forward suspicious emails to phishing@hmrc.gsi.gov.uk and then delete them. It is also important to avoid clicking on websites or links in suspicious emails, or opening attachments.

7. Firms should have policies on cyber security, AML and GDPR.

Taxpayer's responsibility

8. The taxpayer has primary responsibility to submit correct and complete filings to the best of their knowledge and belief. The final decision as to whether to disclose any issue is that of the client but in relation to your responsibilities see paragraph 12 below.

9. In annual self-assessment returns or returns with short filing periods the filing may include reasonable estimates where necessary.

Member's responsibility

10. A member who prepares a filing on behalf of a client is responsible to the client for the accuracy of the filing based on the information provided.

11. In dealing with HMRC in relation to a client's tax affairs a member should bear in mind their duty of confidentiality to the client and that they are acting as the agent of their client. They have a duty to act in the best interests of their client.

12. A member should act in good faith in dealings with HMRC in accordance with the fundamental principle of integrity. In particular the member should take reasonable care and exercise appropriate professional scepticism when making statements or asserting facts on behalf of a client.

13. Where acting as a tax agent, a member is not required to audit the figures in the books and records provided or verify information provided by a client or by a third party. However, a member should take care not to be associated with the presentation of facts they know or believe to be incorrect or misleading, not to assert tax positions in a tax filing which they consider to have no sustainable basis.

14. When a member is communicating with HMRC, they should consider whether they need to make it clear to what extent they are relying on information which has been supplied by the client or a third party.

Materiality

15. Whether an amount is to be regarded as material depends upon the facts and circumstances of each case.

16. The profits of a trade, profession, vocation or property business should be computed in accordance with GAAP subject to any adjustment required or authorised by law in computing profits for those purposes. This permits a trade, profession, vocation or property business to disregard non-material adjustments in computing its accounting profits.

17. The application of GAAP, and therefore materiality does not extend beyond the accounting profits. Thus, the accounting concept of materiality cannot be applied when completing tax filings.

18. It should be noted that for certain small businesses an election may be made to use the cash basis instead; for small property businesses the default position is the cash basis. Where the cash basis is used, materiality is not relevant.

Disclosure

19. If a client is unwilling to include in a tax filing the minimum information required by law, the member should follow the guidance in Help sheet C: Dealing with Errors. The paragraphs below (paras 20 – 24) give guidance on some of the more common areas of uncertainty over disclosure.

20. In general, it is likely to be in a client's own interests to ensure that factors relevant to their tax liability are adequately disclosed to HMRC because:

    - Their relationship with HMRC is more likely to be on a satisfactory footing if they can demonstrate good faith in their dealings with them. HMRC notes in 'Your Charter' that 'We want to give you a service that is fair, accurate and based on mutual trust and respect'; and
    - They will reduce the risk of a discovery or further assessment and may reduce exposure to interest and penalties.

21. It may be advisable to consider fuller disclosure than is strictly necessary. Reference to 'The Standards for Tax Planning' in PCRT may be relevant. The factors involved in making this decision include:
    - A filing relies on a valuation;
    - The terms of the applicable law;
    - The view taken by the member;
    - The extent of any doubt that exists;
    - The manner in which disclosure is to be made; and
    - The size and gravity of the item in question.

22. When advocating fuller disclosure than is necessary a member should ensure that their client is adequately aware of the issues involved and their potential implications. Fuller disclosure should only be made with the client's consent.

23. Cases will arise where there is doubt as to the correct treatment of an item of income or expenditure, or the computation of a gain or allowance. In such cases a member ought to consider what additional disclosure, if any, might be necessary. For example, additional disclosure should be considered where:

- There is inherent doubt as to the correct treatment of an item, for example, expenditure on repairs which might be regarded as capital in whole or part, or the VAT liability of a particular transaction; or
- HMRC has published its interpretation or has indicated its practice on a point, but the client proposes to adopt a different view, whether or not supported by Counsel's opinion. The member should refer to the guidance on the Veltema case and the paragraph below. See also HMRC guidance.

24. A member who is uncertain whether their client should disclose a particular item or of its treatment should consider taking further advice before reaching a decision. They should use their best endeavours to ensure that the client understands the issues, implications and the proposed course of action. Such a decision may have to be justified at a later date, so the member's files should contain sufficient evidence to support the position taken, including timely notes of discussions with the client and/or with other advisors, copies of any second opinion obtained and the client's final decision. A failure to take reasonable care may result in HMRC imposing a penalty if an error is identified after an enquiry.

Supporting documents

25. For the most part, HMRC does not consider that it is necessary for a taxpayer to provide supporting documentation in order to satisfy the taxpayer's overriding need to make a correct filing. HMRC's view is that, where it is necessary for that purpose, explanatory information should be entered in the 'white space' provided on the filing. However, HMRC does recognise that the taxpayer may wish to supply further details of a particular computation or transaction in order to minimise the risk of a discovery assessment being raised at a later time. Following the uncertainty created by the decision in Veltema, HMRC's guidance can be found in SP1/06 - Self Assessment: Finality and Discovery.

26. Further HMRC guidance says that sending attachments with a tax filing is intended for those cases where the taxpayer 'feels it is crucial to provide additional information to support the filing but for some reason cannot utilise the white space'.

Reliance on HMRC published guidance

27. Whilst it is reasonable in most circumstances to rely on HMRC published guidance, a member should be aware that the Tribunal and the courts will apply the law even if this conflicts with HMRC guidance.

28. Notwithstanding this, if a client has relied on HMRC guidance which is clear and unequivocal and HMRC resiles from any of the terms of the guidance, a Judicial Review claim is a possible route to pursue.

Approval of tax filings

29. The member should advise the client to review their tax filing before it is submitted.

30. The member should draw the client's attention to the responsibility which the client is taking in approving the filing as correct and complete. Attention should be drawn to any judgmental areas or positions reflected in the filing to ensure that the client is aware of these and their implications before they approve the filing.

31. A member should obtain evidence of the client's approval of the filing in electronic or non-electronic form.

4. PCRT Help sheet B: Tax advice

The Standards for Tax Planning

1. The Standards for Tax Planning are critical to any planning undertaken by members. They are:

   - Client Specific

     Tax planning must be specific to the particular client's facts and circumstances. Clients must be alerted to the wider risks and implications of any courses of action.

   - Lawful

     At all times members must act lawfully and with integrity and expect the same from their clients. Tax planning should be based on a realistic assessment of the facts and on a credible view of the law.

     Members should draw their client's attention to where the law is materially uncertain, for example because HMRC is known to take a different view of the law. Members should consider taking further advice appropriate to the risks and circumstances of the particular case, for example where litigation is likely.

   - Disclosure and transparency

     Tax advise must not rely for its effectiveness on HMRC having less than the relevant facts. Any disclosure must fairly represent all relevant facts.

   - Tax planning arrangements

     Members must not create, encourage or promote tax planning arrangements or structures that i) set out to achieve results that are contrary to the clear intention of Parliament in enacting relevant legislation and/or ii) are highly artificial or highly contrived and seek to exploit shortcomings within the relevant legislation.

   - Professional judgement and appropriate documentation

   - Applying these requirements to particular client advisory situations requires members to exercise professional judgement on a number of matters. Members should keep notes on a timely basis of the rationale for the judgements exercised in seeking to adhere to these requirements

Guidance

2. The paragraphs below provide guidance for members when considering whether advice complies with the Fundamental Principles and Standards for Tax Planning.

Tax evasion

3. A member should never be knowingly involved in tax evasion, although, of course, it is appropriate to act for a client who is rectifying their affairs.

Tax planning and advice

4. In contrast to tax evasion, tax planning is legal. However, under the Standard members 'must not create, encourage or promote tax planning arrangements that (i) set out to achieve results that are contrary to the clear intention of Parliament in enacting relevant legislation and/or (ii) are highly artificial or highly contrived and seek to exploit shortcomings within the relevant legislation'.

5. Things to consider:
   - Have you checked that your engagement letter fully covers the scope of the planning advice?
   - Have you taken the Standards for Tax Planning and the Fundamental Principles into account? Is it client specific? Is it lawful? Will all relevant facts be disclosed to HMRC? Is it creating, encouraging or promoting tax planning contrary to the 4th Standard for Tax Planning.
   - How tax sophisticated is the client?
   - Has the client made clear what they wish to achieve by the planning?
   - What are the issues involved with the implementation of the planning?
   - What are the risks associated with the planning and have you warned the client of the them? For example:
     - The strength of the legal interpretation relied upon.
     - The potential application of the GAAR.
     - The implications for the client, including the obligations of the client in relation to their tax return, if the planning requires disclosure under DOTAS or DASVOIT and the potential for an accelerated payment notice or partner payment notice?
     - The reputational risk to the client and the member of the planning in the public arena.
     - The stress, cost and wider personal or business implications to the client in the event of a prolonged dispute with HMRC. This may involve unwelcomed publicity, costs, expenses and loss of management time over a significant period.
     - If the client tenders for government contracts, the potential impact of the proposed tax planning on tendering for and retaining public sector contracts.
     - The risk of counteraction. This may occur before the planning is completed or potentially there may be retrospective counteraction at a later date.
     - The risk of challenge by HMRC. Such challenge may relate to the legal interpretation relied upon, but may alternatively relate to the construction of the facts, including the implementation of the planning.
     - The risk and inherent uncertainty of litigation. The probability of the planning being overturned by the courts if litigated and the potential ultimate downside should the client be unsuccessful.
     - Is a second opinion necessary/advisable?
   - Are the arrangements in line with any applicable code of conduct or ethical guidelines or stances for example the Banking Code, and fit and proper tests for charity trustees and pension administrators?
   - Are you satisfied that the client understands the planning proposed?
   - Have you documented the advice given and the reasoning behind it?

5. PCRT Help sheet C: Dealing with errors

Introduction

1. For the purposes of this guidance, the term 'error' is intended to include all errors and mistakes whether they were made by the client, the member, HMRC or any other party involved in a client's tax affairs, and whether made innocently or deliberately.

2. During a member's relationship with the client, the member may become aware of possible errors in the client's tax affairs. Unless the client is already aware of the possible error, they should be informed as soon as the member identifies them.

3. Where the error has resulted in the client paying too much tax the member should advise the client to make a repayment claim. The member should advise the client of the time limits to make a claim and have regard to any relevant time limits. The rest of this Help sheet deals with situations where tax may be due to HMRC.

4. Sometimes an error made by HMRC may mean that the client has not paid tax actually due or they have been incorrectly repaid tax. There may be fee costs as a result of correcting such mistakes. A member should bear in mind that, in some circumstances, clients or agents may be able to claim for additional professional costs incurred and compensation from HMRC.

5. A member should act correctly from the outset. A member should keep sufficient appropriate records of discussions and advice and when dealing with errors the member should:
   - give the client appropriate advice';
   - if necessary, so long as they continue to act for the client, seek to persuade the client to behave correctly;
   - take care not to appear to be assisting a client to plan or commit any criminal offence or to conceal any offence which has been committed; and
   - in appropriate situations, or where in doubt, discuss the client's situation with a colleague or an independent third party (having due regard to client confidentiality).

6. Once aware of a possible error, a member must bear in mind the legislation on money laundering and the obligations and duties which this places upon them.

7. Where the member may have made the error, the member should consider whether they need to notify their professional indemnity insurers.

8. In any situation where a member has concerns about their own position, they should consider taking specialist legal advice. For example, where a client appears to have used the member to assist in the commissioning of a criminal offence and people could question whether the member had acted honestly in in good faith. Note that The Criminal Finances Act 2017 has created new criminal offences of failure to prevent facilitation of tax evasion.

9. The flowchart below summarises the recommended steps a member should take where a possible error arises. It must be read in conjunction with the guidance and commentary that follow it.

Dealing with errors flowchart

6. PCRT Help sheet D: Requests for data by HMRC

Introduction

1. For the purposes of this help sheet the term 'data' includes documents in whatever form (including electronic) and other information. While this guidance relates to HMRC requests, other government bodies or organisations may also approach the member for data. The same principles apply.

2. A distinction should be drawn between a request for data made informally ('informal requests') and those requests for data which are made in exercise of a power to require the provision of the data requested ('formal requests').

3. Similarly, requests addressed to a client and those addressed to a member require different handling.

4. Where a member no longer acts for a client, the member remains subject to the duty of confidentiality. In relation to informal requests, the member should refer the enquirer either to the former client or if authorised by the client to the new agent. In relation to formal requests addressed to the member, the termination of their professional relationship with the client does not affect the member's duty to comply with that request, where legally required to do so.

5. A member should comply with formal requests and should not seek to frustrate legitimate requests for information. Adopting a constructive approach may help to resolve issues promptly and minimise costs to all parties.

6. Whilst a member should be aware of HMRC's powers it may be appropriate to take specialist advice.

7. Devolved tax authorities have separate powers.

8. Two flowcharts are at the end of this help sheet;
   - Requests for data addressed to the member, and
   - Requests for data addressed to the client.

Informal requests addressed to the client

9. From time to time HMRC chooses to communicate directly with clients rather than with the appointed agent.

10. HMRC has given reassurances that it is working to ensure that initial contact on compliance checks will normally be via the agent and only if the agent does not reply within an appropriate timescale will the contact be directly with the client.

11. When the member assists a client in dealing with such requests from HMRC, the member should advise the client that cooperation with informal requests can provide greater opportunities for the taxpayer to find a pragmatic way to work through the issue at hand with HMRC.

Informal requests addressed to the member

12. Disclosure in response to informal requests can only be made with the client's permission.

13. In many instances, the client will have authorised routine disclosure of relevant data, for example, through the engagement letter. However, if there is any doubt about whether the client has authorised disclosure, the member should ask the client to approve what is to be disclosed.

14. Where an oral enquiry is made by HMRC, a member should consider asking for it to be put in writing so that a response may be agreed with the client.

15. Although there is no obligation to comply with an informal request in whole or in part, a member should advise the client whether it is in the client's best interests to disclose such data, as lack of cooperation may have a direct impact on penalty negotiations post—enquiry.

16. Informal requests may be forerunners to formal requests compelling the disclosure of data. Consequently, it may be sensible to comply with such requests.

Formal requests addressed to the client

17. In advising their client a member should consider whether specialist advice may be needed, for example on such issues as whether the notice has been issued in accordance with the relevant tax legislation and whether the data request is valid.

18. The member should also advise the client about any relevant right of appeal against the formal request if appropriate and of the consequences of a failure to comply.

19. If the notice is legally effective the client is legally obliged to comply with the request.

20. The most common statutory notice issued to clients and third parties by HMRC is under Schedule 36 FA 2008.

Formal requests addressed to the member

21. The same principles apply to formal requests to the member as formal requests to clients.

22. If a formal request is valid it **overrides the member's duty of confidentiality** to their client. The member is therefore obliged to comply with the request. Failure to comply with their legal obligations can expose the member to civil or criminal penalties.

23. In cases where the member is not legally precluded by the terms of the notice from communicating with the client, the member should advise the client of the notice and keep the client informed of progress and developments.

24. The member should ensure that in complying with any notice they do not provide information or data outside the scope of the notice.

25. If a member is faced with a situation in which HMRC is seeking to enforce disclosure by the removal of data, or seeking entrance to inspect business premises occupied by a member in their capacity as an adviser, the member should consider seeking immediate professional advice, to ensure that this is the legally correct course of action.

Privileged data

26. Legal privilege arises under common law and may only be overridden if this is set out in legislation. It protects a party's right to communicate in confidence with a legal adviser. The privilege belongs to the client and not to the member.

27. If a document is privileged: The client cannot be required to make disclosure of that document to HMRC. Another party cannot disclose it (including the member), without the client's express permission.

28. There are two types of legal privilege under common law: legal advice privilege and litigation privilege.

(a) Legal advice privilege

Covers documents passing between a client and their legal adviser prepared for the purposes of obtaining or giving legal advice. However, communications from a tax adviser who is not a practising lawyer will not attract legal advice privilege even if such individuals are giving advice on legal matters such as tax law.

(b) Litigation privilege

Covers data created for the dominant purpose of litigation. Litigation privilege may arise where litigation has not begun, but is merely contemplated and may apply to data prepared by non-lawyer advisors (including tax advisors). There are two important limits on litigation privilege. First, it does not arise in respect of non-adversarial proceedings. Second, the documents must be produced for the 'dominant purpose' of litigation.

29. A privilege under Schedule 36 paragraphs 19, (documents relating to the conduct of a pending appeal), 24 and 25 (auditors, and tax advisors' documents) might exist by "quasi-privilege" and if this is the case a tax adviser does not have to provide those documents. Care should be taken as not all data may be privileged.

30. A member who receives a request for data, some of which the member believes may be subject to privilege or 'quasi-privilege', should take independent legal advice on the position, unless expert in this area.

Help sheet D: Flowchart regarding requests for data by HMRC to the Member

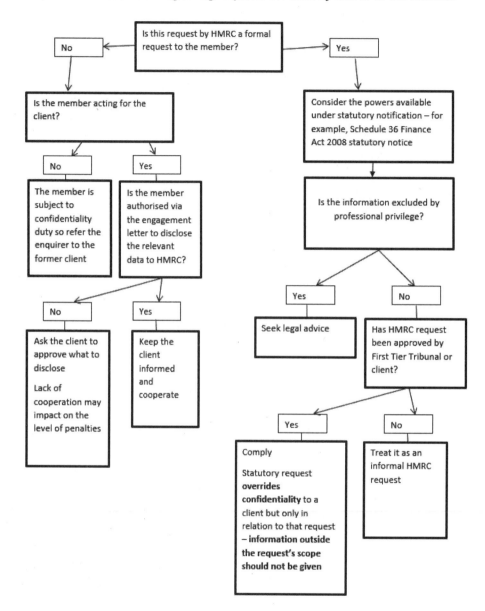

Help sheet D: Flowchart regarding requests for data by HMRC to the Client

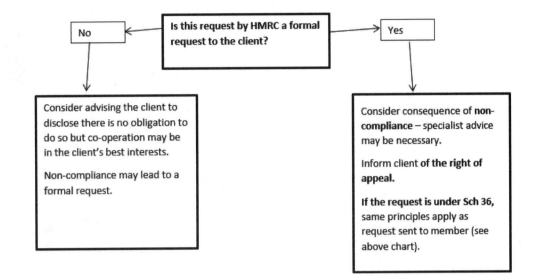

No ← Is this request by HMRC a formal request to the client? → Yes

Consider advising the client to disclose there is no obligation to do so but co-operation may be in the client's best interests.

Non-compliance may lead to a formal request.

Consider consequence of **non-compliance** – specialist advice may be necessary.

Inform client **of the right of appeal.**

If the request is under Sch 36, same principles apply as request sent to member (see above chart).

Reference Material

for AAT Assessment of Personal Tax

Finance Act 2019

Taxation tables for tasks 2-13

For assessments from 1 January – 31 December 2020

Note: this reference material is accessible by candidates during their live computer based assessment for Personal Tax.

Note: Page numbers are those of the original AAT Reference Document

Contents

AAT is a registered charity. No. 1050724

1. Income tax – tax rates and bands

Tax rates	Tax bands	Normal rates %	Dividend rates %
Basic rate	£ 1 - £37,500	20	7.5
Higher rate	£37,501 - £150,000	40	32.5
Additional rate	£150,001 and over	45	38.1

2. Allowances

		£
Personal allowance		12,500
Savings allowance:	Basic rate taxpayer	1,000
	Higher rate taxpayer	500
Dividend allowance		2,000
Income limit for personal allowances*		100,000

* Personal allowances are reduced by £1 for every £2 over the income limit.

3. Property allowance

	£
Annual limit	1,000

4. Individual savings accounts

	£
Annual limit	20,000

aat

5.   Car benefit percentage

Emissions for petrol engines	%
0g/km to 50g/km	16
51g/km to 75 g/km	19
76g/km to 94g/km	22
95g/km or more	23 + 1% for every extra 5g/km above 95g/km
Diesel engines*	Additional 4%

* The additional 4% will not apply to diesel cars which are registered on or after 1 September 2017 and they meet the RDE2 standards.

6.   Car fuel benefit

	£
Base figure	24,100

7.   Approved mileage allowance payments (employees and residential landlords)

First 10,000 miles	45p per mile
Over 10,000 miles	25p per mile
Additional passengers	5p per mile per passenger
Motorcycles	24p per mile
Bicycles	20p per mile

8.   Van scales charge

	£
Basic charge	3,430
Private fuel charge	655

	%
Benefit charge for zero emission vans	60

9. Other benefits in kind

Expensive accommodation limit	£75,000
Health screening	One per year
Incidental overnight expenses: within UK	£5 per night
Incidental overnight expenses: overseas	£10 per night
Job-related accommodation	£Nil
Living expenses where job-related exemption applies	Restricted to 10% of employees net earnings
Loan of assets annual charge	20%
Low-rate or interest free loans	Up to £10,000
Mobile telephones	One per employee
Non-cash gifts from someone other than the employer	£250 per tax year
Non-cash long service award	£50 per year of service
Pay whilst attending a full time course	£15,480 per academic year
Provision of eye tests and spectacles for VDU use	£Nil
Provision of parking spaces	£Nil
Provision of workplace childcare	£Nil
Provision of workplace sports facilities	£Nil
Removal and relocation expenses	£8,000
Staff party or event	£150 per head
Staff suggestion scheme	Up to £5,000
Subsidised meals	£Nil
Working from home	£4 per week / £18 per month

10. HMRC official rate

HMRC official rate	2.5%

11. National insurance contributions

		%
Class 1 Employee:	Below £8,632	0
	Above £8,632 and Below £50,000	12
	£50,000 and above	2
Class 1 Employer:	Below £8,632	0
	£8,632 and above	13.8
Class 1A		13.8
		£
Employment allowance		3,000

12. Capital gains tax – tax rates

	%
Basic rate	10
Higher rate	20

13. Capital gains tax - exemption

	£
Annual exempt amount	12,000

14. Inheritance tax – tax rates

		£
Nil rate band		325,000
Additional residence nil-rate band*		150,000
		%
Excess taxable at:	Death rate	40
	Lifetime rate	20

* Applies when a home is passed on death to direct descendants of the deceased after 6 April 2017. Any unused band is transferrable to a spouse or civil partner.

15. Inheritance tax – tapering relief

	% reduction
3 years or less	0
Over 3 years but less than 4 years	20
Over 4 years but less than 5 years	40
Over 5 years but less than 6 years	60
Over 6 years but less than 7 years	80

16. Inheritance tax – exemptions

		£
Small gifts		250 per transferee per tax year
Marriage or civil partnership:	From parent	5,000
	Grandparent	2,500
	One party to the other	2,500
	Others	1,000
Annual exemption		3,000

17. Deemed domicile

Deemed domicile	Criteria
Condition A	Was born in the UK
	Domicile of origin was in the UK
	Was resident in the UK for 2017 to 2018 or later years
Condition B	Has been UK resident for at least 15 of the 20 years immediately before the tax year

for your notes

for your notes

for your notes

for your notes

for your notes

for your notes

for your notes

for your notes

for your notes

for your notes

for your notes

for your notes

for your notes

---

for your notes

for your notes

for your notes